# GOLD PANNING

## *IS EASY*

by

### ROY LAGAL

RAM
BOOKS

A RAM GUIDEBOOK B.J. Nelson, Editor

ISBN 0-915920-39-5
*Library of Congress Catalog Card No. 76-11382*
*Gold Panning Is Easy*
©Copyright 1976. ©Copyright rev. 1978 ed. ©Copyright 1980.
Roy Lagal.

First printing August 1976. Fifth printing April 1980.

Printed in U.S.A. by
Yaquinto Printing Co., Inc. • 4809 S. Westmoreland • Dallas, Texas 75237

# CONTENTS

# Complete List of Books
## by the Same Author
## and Publisher

*GOLD PANNING IS EASY*

*DETECTOR OWNER'S FIELD MANUAL*

*HOW TO TEST "Before Buying" DETECTOR FIELD GUIDE (BFO-TR-VLF/TR)*

*HOW TO USE "After Buying" DETECTOR FIELD GUIDE (BFO-TR)*

*ELECTRONIC PROSPECTING (with Charles Garrett and Bob Grant)*

*THE COMPLETE VLF-TR METAL DETECTOR HANDBOOK (All About Ground Canceling Metal Detectors) (with Charles Garrett)*

# FOREWORD

During my many years of association with the mining and treasure hunting industry I have read a number of books about gold panning and prospecting with the metal/mineral detector. These well-written and authoritative books have explained how gold is associated with other earth materials; where to find it; how to reclaim it, both by older methods and by more modern procedures. Some technical experience is necessary to understand much of the terminology used in these volumes. The beginning prospector does *not*, as a rule, have the prior knowledge required to understand the "gold" language and to fill in the gaps left in many of these books. I have always believed the beginner needed something extra ... a guide through the first difficult steps when failure or disappointment are most likely to occur.

Roy Lagal, author, life-long prospector and treasure hunter from Lewiston, Idaho, has fulfilled the need by compiling this large collection of actual in-the-field photographs, each accompanied by a step-by-step instructive procedure written in common everyday language that everyone can understand. There has long been a need for a gold pan designed specifically to aid the beginner and experienced professional alike. Roy has designed such a pan, the "Gravity Trap" gold pan. It has achieved great acceptance and acclaim. It is the most efficient, practical, easiest-to-use gold pan ever built.

Roy also gives detailed instructions in the use of metal/ mineral detectors for prospecting. These proven and successful panning methods and metal detecting tips are certain to aid even the most experienced, plus making it possible for the beginner to start with ease and finish with success. I consider this to be one of the most down-to-earth, practical books for the beginning prospector that I have ever read.

*Charles Garrett*

# PREFACE

If you are between the ages of 8 to 80 you should know what gold is, its general appearance and its approximate value. Even so, a small amount of research will quickly convince you of the tremendous amount of space needed to comment fully on the world's most coveted metal. An entire library would not contain enough room to house this information, and most of it would be of absolutely no use to the average, everyday gold panner or electronic prospector. If you desire more technical information on the metal itself, visit your library or select from several of the professional guides listed in the "Recommended Supplementary Books" section in the back of this book.

*GOLD PANNING IS EASY* deals with the "how and where" methods of panning and prospecting with the metal/ mineral detector . . . steps that are necessary for the beginner to succeed, and, hopefully, it contains many helpful and useful ideas for the old prospector. I have always managed to glean some bit of knowledge from any book or manual I have had the pleasure of reading. Bearing this in mind, I sincerely hope that even the most experienced prospector may profit in some small way by the knowledge in *GOLD PANNING IS EASY.*

I have been besieged with questions from amateurs for years—"How do you pan for gold?" and "Does a metal/mineral detector aid you when prospecting?" Most have admitted to purchasing many books on those subjects, yet have failed to gain the correct or necessary information in their first attempt. I have described the easiest, fastest and most successful methods for both gold panning and detector operation in common, everyday language that anyone should find self-explanatory.

My many years of searching for the yellow metal have produced a wide and varied experience, complete with many failures, yet with many satisfying successes. I know my judgment has been tempered. And, hopefully, I have acquired the necessary patience and expertise so that this small bit of hard-earned knowledge that I pass on to those reading this book will be of value.

Remember, only one thing will ever hold true in your quest for the golden riches, "Gold is where you find it."

# CHAPTER I

# *The Various Types of Pans*

## STEEL PAN CONSTRUCTION

The steel gold pan is manufactured in many styles, in almost any size from two inches wide (yes, two inches!) up to perhaps twenty-four inches wide. They will vary in depth, wall slant and in steel thickness. Some will have small indentations or pressed-in riffle traps intended to slow down or trap the gold. Most "pressed" or "stamped" indentations in the steel pans consist of either a slight bevel from the inside to the outside (forming an oval trough) or a bevel from the outside to the inside (forming an oval ridge). These so-called "riffles" may be short in length, or may extend all the way around the pan. The rounded design of such riffles or traps leaves many doubts as to the effectiveness of this style. Also, many types of "riffles" are constructed with a peak design, with a sharp slope upward and

TYPES OF GOLD PANS: Basically, there are only TWO types of gold pans in use today. They can be quickly described as either *steel* (left two pans in the photograph) or *plastic* (the two on the right). Of course, there are dozens of different design configurations and sizes in both types.

1

then sharply downward, much like an Indian teepee. The action of the water when wet panning creates the same amount of turbulence on BOTH sides of these riffle designs, causing them to lose their effectiveness as gold traps. Since an experienced prospector can pan successfully with almost any type of design (lowly frying pan, pie pan, or any type of modern gold pan), no purpose is served by having these indentations or riffles constructed in ANY type of pan unless the feature definitely AIDS the beginner or SPEEDS UP the professional.

## PLASTIC PAN CONSTRUCTION

Most plastic gold pans are constructed in the same types of configurations and designs as the metal pans. Correct placement of the 90-degree angle or trap is the secret of whether the pan will have a definite advantage when used by the inexperienced beginner. If the water falls over and downward when the pan is used, the *inconsistency* of the water action will clean the "trap" as quickly as it does the rest of the pan. The "drywasher" type of riffle uses the 90-degree angle facing the upward or highest portion of the sluice box. This placement has a distinct advantage if you consider that all or most of the heavier materials will become trapped behind the sharp upward side of the riffle design. This design, on a smaller scale, is also used in "jig" or "floatation" type separation tables used to clean concentrates. If you watch a drywasher or sluice box in operation you will notice that most of the gold becomes trapped in FRONT of the first riffle, provided the downward slope is adjusted correctly. Since any type of design should present ALL OF THE ADVANTAGES POSSIBLE for the beginner, it makes common sense to design the 90-degree angle or trap to face "up hill" toward the highest portion of the pan. It was with all these ideas in mind that I carefully designed the Garrett "Gravity Trap" Gold Pan. The pan is produced in plastic because plastic has many advantages over steel pan construction, as discussed in following paragraphs.

## STEEL *vs.* PLASTIC

While ALL gold pans, plastic or steel, MUST be kept clean, the steel pan must be "burnt" by exposure to extreme heat or flame to remove the natural oily surface and "blue" the surface of the steel. Nitric acid cannot be used in a steel pan to remove magnetic iron from the concentrates because the acid instantly dissolves anything iron. If a magnet is used to remove black sand (magnetic iron) from a steel pan, the magnet tends to stick to the pan itself. When mercury is used to gather the fine

2

To determine if microscopic particles of gold are present in an ore sample, first finely crush the sample in a mortar. Then dump the crushed ore in the green "Gravity Trap" gold pan. With a high power magnifier (10 to 20 power) observe the sample carefully. The gold pan's intermediate green shade shows microscopic particles of gold better than would a darker surface, such as black, or a lighter surface, such as steel.

gold common in some placer operations, it will sometimes become "lost" or coated on the surface of the steel pan. If you have ever tried placing black sand concentrates in a coffee can and then placing mercury with it to gather the fine gold, you will have quickly discovered that the mercury becomes coated or lost on the surface of the "tin." The use of plastic in gold pan construction eliminates all of the acid, magnet, and mercury problems for the prospector.

A plastic pan does not need to be burned. It is generally constructed with a particular sandblasted surface to eliminate the slick surface. (Some plastics have a slick, greasy-appearing surface.) Nitric acid does not harm the plastic, and a magnet will not stick to the surface. Mercury will neither coat, nor become lost on, the plastic pan. Such obvious advantages indicate the use of plastic in the place of steel for gold pan construction. An additional advantage is the much lighter weight of the plastic pan, both to transport and to use.

## COLOR IS IMPORTANT

The old prospector simply "blued" his pan by burning, and thus discovered that the "blued" surface had advantages for visual detection of flour gold over the whiter color of steel. After much experimentation it was discovered that a green color showed gold to the best advantage. If the green is TOO light in color the sun tends to glare on it; if the green is TOO dark it tends to look *black* on cloudy days and small microscopic particles of gold cannot be seen. A Kelly-green was chosen as a compromise to achieve the best all-around results. This color also lets garnets, platinum, sapphires, and other gems and precious metal show better. The end result produced much faster panning time for the true professional and much safer and surer results for the beginner.

I myself have an extensive collection of old gold pans, both copper and steel. I have recovered these from old mining camps over the years. When I saw my first plastic gold pan, I was quite shocked and vowed never to use one. After seeing the obvious advantages of the plastic material over steel I immediately set about to design one for greater speed and better color visibility for fine gold recovery. I offer a piece of sage advice to either the old prospector or the beginner...

Author wet panning in a stream. Gravity can cause gold concentrations to occur anywhere along a stream bed.

4

Author dry panning in ancient river channel high on a mountainside.

always keep an open mind, and if there is an easier and faster way to do a job, then you should look into it. I'm glad I did.

# CHAPTER II

# Gold Pans and Different Panning Methods

Basically, gold pans and gold panning methods have remained unchanged for many thousands of years. As gold is slightly over nineteen times as heavy as water it will sink rapidly and is easily recovered by "panning." Various panning methods were used in the earliest times, and many different types of vessels were employed. Regardless of the length of time that gold has been coveted and used as wealth, the methods of panning remain basically the same. Any type of jar, bowl or metal container, or any type of material, such as a blanket, can be used to recover the heavy metal. In water it can be easily panned or sorted from the lighter weight rocks and dirt as the heavier gold tends to sink quickly down through all the debris, finally coming to rest at the bottom. It also may be recovered by dry methods where water is not available; however, this "dry" washing or panning is not so efficient, and generally only the heavier pieces can be recovered without sophisticated equipment. We will discuss "dry panning" later.

## WET PANNING

Wet panning in water will always follow these general procedures. Place material suspected of containing gold in some type of vessel or container. Place under sufficient water to cover operation; run hands through material to thoroughly wet the bottom and produce a "liquid" state of suspension; rotate the vessel or container under water vigorously in circular motion; remove larger rocks that are washed clean; shake in circular motion, sidewise, front to back, up or down (it all achieves the same result); let lighter material "spill" off gradually; finally there is only the heavier material (concentrates) left in the bottom. Crudely put? Yes. Simple? Yes. This has been going on for many thousands of years with improved expertise and improved containers (pans or vessels) making it easier. Regardless of whether I or anyone else outlines detailed instructions to save you time and effort, you will have to follow the basic procedures given above.

## DRY PANNING

Dry washing or dry panning will also follow a basic set of procedures. For example, place a blanket on the ground and shovel dry material suspected of containing coarse gold onto it. Two people then grasp the ends of the blanket firmly and proceed to "pull" the blanket back and forth between them. The heavier particles of gold will settle through the debris and come to rest on the blanket. Pick off the top material, and carry home the heavier concentrates for wet washing and further examination. A metal vessel or container is handled with the same basic procedure. Shake firmly, pick and spill off the lighter material, and you have saved the heavier concentrates for later classification.

## GRAVITY MAKES IT POSSIBLE

Regardless of explicit instructions involving wet panning or dry washing, the weight of the heavier gold will always produce these end results. Speed may be gained by use of specialized pans and dry washers, and better results may be obtained by following specific panning procedures; but the reason why it all happens still remains the same. GRAVITY forces the heavier gold and other precious metals to the bottom of ANY vessel or container, the same as gravity forces these heavier elements to the bottom of river beds until they are stopped by bedrock.

## DIFFERENT PANNING METHODS

The invention of the GARRETT "GRAVITY TRAP" PAN has made it possible for the beginner to pan like an expert. This exceptional time-saver was not designed and marketed as a "trick" gold pan. Charles Garrett of Garrett Electronics has a reputation worldwide as a purveyor of only the highest-quality merchandise. My own reputation in the treasure hunting and prospecting fields has never been marred by false claims. We are so positive we have designed and produced the most advanced time-saving tool for the professional prospector and beginner that we have personally autographed this fantastic pan. The Garrett "Gravity Trap" Gold Pan is personally used and demonstrated by George Massie, President of Gold Prospectors Association of America, a national organization. They teach mining methods and demonstrate advanced equipment in seminars throughout the U.S.

In the following instructions intended for the beginning prospector, you will notice that the methods and procedures closely resemble the same methods used with conventional

Vacationing family pans for gold in running stream somewhere in the U.S.A. It is possible to find gold in every state. The "Gravity Trap" gold pan enables you to check likely streams in your locale.

pans, either steel or plastic. Any experienced panner would need no such instructions for, as mentioned before, this is a time-saving tool, NOT a trick pan. The "Gravity Trap" riffles will help the experienced panner to pan twice or three times as much, and they enable the beginner to have complete confidence so that he will immediately begin "saving" gold. This is a feat that would take him some time to learn with conventional pans containing inferior riffles, *or perhaps NO true "Gravity Trap"* advantages at all. Several professional mining organizations conduct Dry Panning and Wet Panning Schools. These schools, or seminars, thoroughly explain the difference between trick panning and the correct panning methods of working in creek-run gravel that may contain many large and small rocks, mud and possibly clay, or possibly an over-abundance of black magnetic sand. These conditions will differ greatly from your practice sessions conducted at home, perhaps in your wash tub. The professional panners who instruct correctly use creek-run gravel with sand and muck mixed in, just as it comes from the gravel deposit. They will slowly and carefully show you how to utilize the gravity traps with the utmost speed *without* losing the finer gold. You would find

LAGAL WINS—Lawrence Lagal holds the Garrett "Gravity Trap" gold pan with which he won the gold panning contest at the 2nd Annual Northwest Treasure Hunt in Spokane, Washington. At the Hunt, attended by over 2,000 treasure hunters and gold enthusiasts, Lawrence competed against gold panners from throughout the United States and Canada. He stated he could not have won without the "Gravity Trap" gold pan.

9

George Massie (center), President of Gold Prospectors Association of America, and Nelson Darling (left), stop in to visit Charles Garrett, President of Garrett Electronics. Mr. Massie, who presents gold mining seminars throughout the entire U. S., dropped in during his annual tour to congratulate Mr. Garrett on the Garrett "Gravity Trap" gold pan. The "Gravity Trap" gold pan is demonstrated and recommended by GPAA.

these seminars extremely educational especially if you should be able to attend one conducted by the Gold Prospectors Association of America. They conduct thoroughly professional classes with emphasis on *successful gold panning* using only actual *creek-run gravel*.

You should also bear in mind that if you set up your own practice sessions in a simulated condition, you should try to use sand, gravel and muck in a combination sufficient to emulate actual conditions. Also in "dry" panning practice, attempt to formulate your own personal style. Remember, almost no TWO panners use EXACTLY the same identical "twist," "pitch" or "motion," yet EVERYONE has to follow a basic rule: you must help the gold or other precious metals that are heavier to find their way to the bottom of whatever type vessel or pan you are using. Many national and state gold panning championships will not allow the use of the "Gravity Trap" pan as to do so would give the owner or user a definite advantage in speed. However, the Garrett "Gravity Trap" pan was allowed in the Northwest Treasure Meet held in Spokane, Washington, in 1974-75, and in the World Championship Meet held in Colorado Springs, Colorado.

*Pictured below are contestants in one of the numerous state and national contests sponsored by GOLD PROSPECTORS ASSOCIATION OF AMERICA. GPAA conducts continuous instruction seminars throughout the U.S., teaching modern-day panning methods and demonstrating the latest equipment for the recreational miner and treasure hunter. Reprinted courtesy GPAA.*

## RULES OF THE CONTEST

PANS: Each contestant will start with a Garrett Positive "Gravity Trap" Gold Pan provided by the contest committee.

GOLD NUGGETS: Eight pea-sized gold nuggets, provided by the contest committee, will be placed on the sand, then the judge will push them into the sand to his first knuckle.

PROCEDURE: Beginning with pan of nuggets and sand, each contestant must remove ALL material (sand) except nuggets by panning.

TIMING: Timing begins when the panner touches the sides of the pan. Timing ends when the panner yells "GOLD." There will be 3 timers.

JUDGING: After the contestant indicates he or she has finished, a judge will count the number of nuggets and insure that there is no sand remaining in the pan. A ten (10) second penalty will be assessed for each lost nugget. There is a limit of 2 minutes.

TOP TEN PRELIMINARY WINNERS will pan in the Championship pan-offs.

CASH PRIZES will be computed from the entry fees to this contest and put into a pool.           1st place—Trophy & 50% of cash pool;
2nd place—Trophy & 20% of cash pool;
3rd place—Trophy & 10% of cash pool;
4th to 10th place will split remainder of pool.

THERE WILL BE A PRACTICE AREA SET UP FOR CONTESTANTS

The winner of GPAA's Oregon State Championship will automatically be entered in The Oregon State Open Championship in Baker this fall.

Columbia Basin Chapter #4 members, Natalie and Frank Meckle, were lucky enough to attend The Oregon State Panning Championship at Baker last fall. Participants were fourteen finalists from all over the state and included one woman and one teenaged young man. The winner was Jack Roberts, who also won the 1975 National Championship.

First Prize was a $189 Metal Detector, and all contestants were given the pan that they used.

(For more information on membership and a FREE copy of their prospecting and treasure hunting publication, write to ... GOLD PROSPECTORS ASSOCIATION OF AMERICA, P. O. Box 507, Bonsall, California 92003.)

11

# CHAPTER III

# *Wet Panning Instructions*

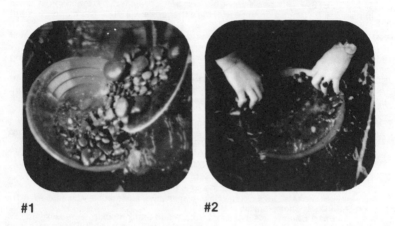

#1                                        #2

ONE. You must obtain some material for panning. If you are removing this from under or beneath water, dig down and discard the loose gravel until you hit firm gravel or bedrock, if possible. Conditions will vary greatly, but most gold will have accumulated on bedrock, having been stopped by this impassable barrier. Do not accept this as always being the case, for many times the gold is deposited in certain layers of different "sized" gravel and at different times. However, the most likely places are on bedrock and behind or downstream from large boulders. Be careful when lifting the gravel out of the water. The water tends to "pan" or sort the gold while on your shovel and the gold can be lost back into the stream. Do not overload your pan.

If you are obtaining the material from a dry bank or gravel bar try to find bedrock if possible. Use a screwdriver or other small tool for digging down in the smallest crevices. A small broom or garden trowel is handy to sweep the material onto your shovel. Continue this cleaning of the bedrock until you have enough to fill your pan approximately one-half to two-thirds full. If it is impossible to reach bedrock, attempt to find areas behind large boulders, perhaps, a deposit in the gravel where it is noticeably "tighter." This indicates a spot that may have held the gold in place when the gravel bar was originally deposited. If the face of the gravel bank is visible you will probably notice many layers of different-colored sand and gravel. Test each one of these layers as they may range far apart in time of deposit. Some may contain gold colors, and some may be barren. As the true saying goes, "Gold is where you find it." It may be anywhere, perhaps in plain old dirt or far up on the side of some mountain. It could have come from a decomposed ore pocket or vein, or it could have been dropped off from some ancient glacier millions of years ago. Panning with a "Gravity Trap" pan does not take much time so be sure to check many different, likely-looking spots.

Perhaps it is impossible to venture forth into the country, but still, you wish to try your new pan. You may use small birdshot (BB's) to simulate gold. The weight is not *equal*, but if you can save the BB's after a few practice sessions you will be proficient enough to head for the hills with increased confidence. Use sand or gravel from around your home, and try to get a mixture that would resemble small pebbles and sand from actual creek bottoms. Place your BB's into this mixture, taking care not to overload your pan while learning. You are now ready for the next step.

TWO. If you are using a large wash tub or other large water container for your practice sessions, place the pan down in the water, making certain it is covered. If you are on a creek or river bank, place the pan in some shallow area where the water is deep enough to completely cover the pan. Be extremely careful not to pick a spot where the current is too swift for this will make your panning difficult and risky. If you are on a creek and the water is too deep to place the pan safely on the bottom, grasp it between your legs and hold it firmly. At first this may seem difficult, but when you are in a squatting position it is easily accomplished as the back of your upper thighs will help hold the pan and keep it from tipping forward. Rubber boots will keep the feet dry since you will generally place your feet forward in the water and squat or sit on some handy rock. If you are not wearing boots and do not wish to get your feet wet, you can hunker down on shore and attempt to bend over

13

enough to accomplish the panning. (However, sometimes this can become very tiring on your back.)

With your pan immersed under water, quickly plunge your hands through the panning material, completely down to the bottom of the pan. Thoroughly mix the contents, permitting the water to wet the entire material. Take care to wash any large rocks, roots, or moss quickly, but carefully, and discard all this from the pan. If clay chunks or talc (talc is a white, sticky-looking substance, much like clay) are present, you will have to carefully keep "squeezing" and washing these chunks until they are completely dissolved. Be sure to keep all this action directly OVER the pan to prevent any loss of gold into open water. These talc and clay chunks are great gold robbers (much like mercury), and will quickly gather your gold while in the pan. If they are discarded before being thoroughly dissolved, they will probably get more gold than you do. The quicker you accomplish the thorough wetting of the entire material, the quicker the gold has a chance to settle. Shaking the pan before the material becomes thoroughly wet and in a complete state of liquid suspension generally accomplishes nothing but to let some of the discolored water and mud flow off. Get to the business *quickly* of thoroughly wetting the entire contents. ONLY THEN do the heavier concentrates (gold) have a chance to *settle*. The contents are now in a completely "liquid" state; the larger rocks and excess debris have been discarded (before shaking); and only a few seconds have been consumed. You will be much faster next time as you become more sure of preventing loss. You are now ready for the next step.

THREE. While holding the pan under water move the entire pan in a circular motion. Do this firmly and strongly, but do NOT let any of the contents slip back into the water (yet). At first, the water on *top* of the material will start swirling, then the entire contents of the pan will start revolving in a circular motion. NOW the heavier gold has a chance to start settling as the material becomes "loose" and the state of liquid suspension is increased. When the material has become thoroughly loosened, perhaps after a quick five to ten such vigorous motions, set the pan down and repeat Step Two where you discarded the larger rocks or debris. (Remember to make certain all rocks and other objects are thoroughly washed clean before discarding.) You may do this rather quickly as long as you let the smaller rocks "sift" through your fingers *back* into the pan. Repeat above swirling procedure.

It is safe at this point to start "spilling off," or letting the

14

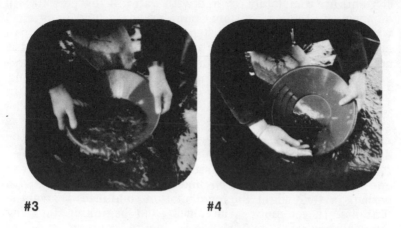

#3            #4

very top of the contents slowly spill over the downward rim of the pan. Point the "Gravity Trap" riffles downward, away from you, in the 12:00 position so all lighter, but thoroughly cleaned material must pass over them. Continue the swirling motion (under water) while carefully letting the cleaned small rocks and sand spill continually over the lower edge of the pan. You may vary this to a side-to-side motion, or you may combine the circular motion with the side-to-side motion. There is definitely NO set procedure as you will quickly develop your own particular style after you become more confident and experienced. The most important motion is to tilt the pan's forward edge occasionally back upward toward yourself. This action causes the material to return to the bottom, or center, of the pan. It also helps to gather the gold and concentrates, and keeps them buried under, and protected from, the loose overburden that is being continually spilled off over the lower rim of the pan.

At this point, the side-to-side motion is perhaps best. The pan and contents are now much lighter. A few panners will use a shuffling fore-and-aft motion, possibly combined with the side-to-side method. Regardless of how you eventually fit these numerous panning techniques into your own particular style, remember always to let GRAVITY work for you, not against you. Never raise the pan's edge above the water unless the contents are completely covered with water. A few persons will demonstrate their exceptional panning speed (and ignorance) while spilling off tightly-packed damp sand, holding the pan high (and dry) in the air. The material is wet, yes, but if it is not in a state of liquid suspension the gold cannot settle regardless of any type of shaking action. It will slide off along with the sand. You can verify this by catching the discards in another pan and repanning after such a wasted effort. The "Gravity Trap" riffles managed to catch whatever gold was deep enough to pass over them, but they had no control over the gold that was mixed in the top sand and gravel being dumped.

At this point the pan is still approximately one-fourth to one-half full. Continue the circular or side-to-side motion, with perhaps a very slight diagonal motion combined. Watch the contents. If you notice the black sand beginning to show through the surface material, it is time to "regroup" and "resettle" the contents once more. Tilt the pan's forward rim upward, and bring the material back toward the center of pan while continuing the shaking motion. (Make sure at all times the material is covered with water.) Tilt the pan forward again while shaking, and continue to spill off the top layer of lighter sand and gravel that works its way to the top. The heavier material settles quickly to the bottom while the lighter material comes to the top. Your only safeguard is to watch closely the material being spilled off. The instant the black sand or heavier concentrates begin to show through, *quickly* bring the entire contents back to the center of the pan and repeat the shaking and spilling off all over again.

It is well to note here that you have probably been very *slow* on your first try. This is well and good. It is better to learn correctly, however slowly. You will have much greater confidence the next time around. Actually, it would have been almost impossible for you to have lost any of the "heaviest" gold unless you deliberately became careless and shook the pan with a fore-and-aft bouncing motion. Such a motion would have caused the gold to roll up and over the "Gravity Trap" riffles. The riffles would have been prevented from doing their job, much the same as a sluice box would be if the operator allows his sluice to become overloaded so that the gravel and muck simply bounce on through. Regardless of the type of sluicing method or panning procedure used, the material must be allowed to pass in contact over the riffles to permit the force of gravity to settle and trap the heaviest concentrates. Gravity

16

easily traps the heaviest gold in front of a sharp 90-degree riffle design, provided the gold has a chance to come in contact with the riffles by settling down through the gravel and sand. Otherwise, the lighter gold and *sometimes even the heavier gold* will just continue to roll along the same as do debris and muck on the bottom of a stream or river bed. This settling principle is the same one that allows the forces of gravity to trap gold in small cracks and behind large boulders in stream beds. Smooth bedrock seldom has any gold trapped on its surface. Certainly this holds true with smooth gold pans that do not have riffles. Only the skilled operator's expertise and knowledge of panning methods would make gold recovery possible with smooth pans.

Your next few pans will be much faster, and eventually you will cut the time of this particular step down to a few seconds. The heavier weight of gold will cause it to sink very quickly (if given a chance), and the "Gravity Trap" riffles will definitely prevent *all* loss, even when using speed methods, if the riffles are allowed to work properly.

You should now have approximately two to four cups of mixed concentrates and small gravel left in the pan. Remember that throughout this last step you should have kept the pan under water or at least the portion or section of the pan that contained the material.

FOUR. I cannot overstress that this next step is a critical one. You must pay attention and learn it perfectly. It is so EASY to become over-confident at this point and simply shake or spill the heavier concentrates over the pan rim. Oh yes, you will still have some gold in your pan when finished, but if you check the discards (tailings) you may find more there than in the pan. The "Gravity Trap" riffles were designed *to catch MORE, finer gold* than any other pan made, but, even so, let's not ignore the basic facts and principles of gravity. At this step there will be mostly heavy black sand concentrates and very little pea-gravel. It will be more difficult for the gold to settle through the heavy, tightly-packed, black sand. The material in your pan now also corresponds closely to the same amount of concentrates that you would have removed from your sluice box.

You should now understand why speed panning in side-shows is not conducted with heavy concentrations of black sand and creek-run gravel. It would make the task of settling the gold slower and much more difficult. While the "Gravity Trap" pan will make the sluice box cleanup process two to three times as fast, common sense dictates that we save ALL the gold, not just part. There would be no point in working your sluice all

17

day, then panning the contents carelessly, losing your hard-earned gold. If you are ever in mining country and see black sand concentrates being panned back into a wash tub or other water container, notice how difficult it is to get the gold to settle through the heavy black sand. Sometimes it is necessary to put a few teaspoons of chlorine bleach into the water. This tends to cut the surface tension of the natural oil on the gold so that it will settle to the bottom. Now let's proceed, keeping in mind that the concentrates *could* be heavily loaded with black sand.

As already stated, you now have approximately two to four cups of small gravel and concentrates. Keep the pan either under water, or partly full of water, and use your swirling or shaking motion to make certain the concentrates are fully settled. Tilt the pan downward (away from you) and shake side-to-side, with perhaps a bit of forward or slight circular motion, letting the light sand and larger pebbles wash off gently. The slight forward motion that you add to your side-to-side motion should be VERY slight as this fore-and-aft motion will tend to roll the contents over the 90-degree riffles preventing the concentrates from being trapped. However, this *slight* forward motion is helpful to start the lighter surface material moving off the pan. Tilt the pan upward and backward toward yourself quite frequently. This keeps bringing the concentrates BACK to the bottom of the pan and tends to keep them buried on the bottom, preventing their loss.

*Watch closely* as the black sand starts to show through the light-colored sand and small pebbles. This is your instant indicator that *it is time to resettle the contents back to the bottom of the pan.* Keep repeating this process while using the side-to-side motion or perhaps your own preferred, yet undeveloped, style and let the lighter material slip over the edge. Another technique is to dip the contents under the water and raise the pan quickly, letting the water action carry off the lighter material. This is the same procedure used with conventional pans, and it is used on the "Gravity Trap" pan by many experienced professionals. Occasionally you will find that some of the heavier small rocks will not wash or slip over the pan's edge without endangering the loss of your heavier concentrates. Simply hold the pan and contents under water with the pan tilted downward and with your free hand carefully rake off these heavier rocks. There is NO danger of raking off any gold with the rocks, as long as you keep the contents under water.

After some practice you will perform this entire step with

the "Gravity Trap" pan *in a matter of seconds.* Continued practice will give you the confidence needed to quickly brush the troublesome rocks and light material off the top at almost any point you may desire. There is a sixth sense that seems to tell the experienced gold panner when the gold has settled to the bottom. When this feeling strikes, go ahead and dump or rake the top off. At first, it may seem certain that you have lost some gold, but by repanning your discards it will become evident you did not. You will quickly learn one thing ... the 90-degree riffle trap permits such speed. You must, however, always be sure that the riffles are in a downward or 12:00 position. They are your only insurance against loss from excessive speed or careless panning. When Step Four is completed, you may have one or two cups of almost pure concentrates containing black sand, hematite and perhaps garnets, sapphires or other gems, and metals common to the area. You may wish to dump these concentrates into another container and finish your panning at home.

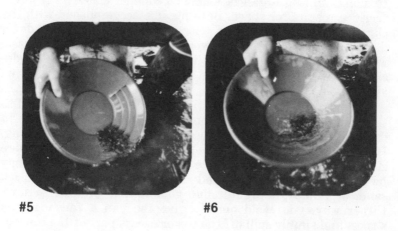

#5          #6

FIVE. You now have some amount of heavy concentrates which have already been cleaned of light sand and small gravel by Step Four. The only task remaining is to achieve the most efficiency from the 90-degree riffle traps. This is one of the easier procedures as you can now observe the action of the contents and tell when you have the gold completely settled. Do not forget to follow the basic procedures; that is, keep the edge of the pan containing the material under the water while shaking or slipping off the black sand. It matters not what shaking style or motion you use. There is one *irrefutable* fact: the material MUST be immersed or covered by water in the pan to create a liquid suspension. This permits the gold to settle downward, especially through the heavy black sand. Failure to do this will allow the gold to remain stationary in the damp or wet sand and quickly slip out of the pan along with the sand. Even though the riffle traps are 90-degrees, the gold mixed with only damp or wet sand will roll merrily along like a giant mud ball, and gravity will be prevented from playing any part in the separation of the heavier metals.

If you should attend one of the many local or state gold panning championships sponsored by the numerous prospecting clubs, you will notice the winner must recover a certain number of gold nuggets more quickly than anyone else. Professional mining organizations who conduct classes will never sacrifice results for speed. Both may be accomplished with the Garrett "Gravity Trap" pan, but you must settle the gold down deep, where the riffles can work. You must utilize the basic facts of gravity, thus permitting the pan to do what it is designed to do. Both exceptional speed and 100%-recovery of all visible gold is possible.

Constantly keep in mind that you have now progressed to the point where you have either gold or nothing. If you are in the field taking potluck on prospecting, you may have nothing. If you are panning the concentrates from a suction dredge cleanup, you will probably have at least a small amount. It may be a heavier type of gold and settle easily through the black sand, or it may be lighter fine gold that is difficult to save. Either way, you could quickly give the pan a few vigorous shakes and simply spill off the top or excess part of the concentrates, and you would have without question trapped most of the gold behind the sharp 90-degree riffles. However, this makes absolutely no sense to the experienced prospector, and, if you were to attempt to demonstrate your speed and expertise on *his* dredge cleanup, you would possibly get a shovel over your head. Gold is simply too valuable to toss back into the stream bed (especially after all the hard work of getting it out).

If you are panning a dredge cleanup it is always wise to place another pan down under the water and let your discards or tailings fall into that pan. This makes it easy to double-check whether you have lost any gold. After a few practice sessions with the "Gravity Trap" pan you will, however, gain confidence that this is no longer necessary.

Author quickly dumping the concentrates from dredging operation into a can for a more leisurely separation later. The fantastic lightweight dredge shown is the Oregon Super Jet 2" model. Purchase or dealer information on this very efficient dredge may be obtained by writing Oregon Gold Dredge, Ltd., P.O. Box 10214, Eugene, Oregon 97402.

Make sure there is sufficient water in the pan to cover the concentrates, either by dipping some in or keeping the pan under the water. (Again, never forget this basic fact of gravity: gold will not sink quickly unless in liquid suspension.) Start using a gentle, side-to-side motion to settle the gold. This side-to-side motion will produce a slight orbiting of the contents as the pan is circular. This slight orbiting motion is helpful at this point, but TOO much rotating would simply cause the gold to roll forward TOO fast and escape the riffle traps by not having time to settle down deep enough. The *gentle* side-to-side motion will cause the gold to sink quickly down BEHIND the sharp riffles. As long as you do not become careless and introduce any pitching or tossing motion into your actions, the gold will remain securely trapped there. You may observe the fine gold (or practice BB's) slowly settle deeper as you continue shaking the pan. Allow the lighter material to slowly slip out of the pan, but never allow the gold (or BB's) to escape.

21

SIX. Occasionally tilt the forward edge of the pan upward and back toward you while continuing the shaking motion. This causes the heavier concentrates to gather or become regrouped back in the bottom of the pan and allows the sharp riffle design to stop them as you again lower the pan forward. You must remember to keep these concentrates covered with water. You will notice fine colors or practice BB's showing through each time you regroup the material. You will also be able to judge how much action is best to cause them to sink. You may experiment by using a fore-and-aft motion, a diagonal, pitching, or tossing motion, or any variation of these motions as you develop your own style. You will find that the gentle side-to-side motion perhaps allows the fine gold to stay trapped behind the 90-degree riffles better and more safely, but you will develop your own particular style after you gain confidence. Remember, *the gravity trap pan will not lose the gold.*

Keep lowering the pan into the water while shaking gently and let the lighter material continue to spill off. Visual observation during this procedure permits great speed as you are able to observe the gold or BB's sink quickly and become firmly trapped behind the sharp riffles. You can accomplish this same step or cleanup procedure in a matter of seconds after only a few practice attempts. However, remember to repan your discards or tailings at this step because you are at the point of no return after you have once discarded the black sand concentrates.

SEVEN. Now only the gold and some of the heaviest concentrates, perhaps silver flakes, garnets, sapphires, platinum (or practice BB's) are left. A small amount of the heavier magnetic black sand still remains so it is time to discontinue using the riffles. The 90-degree "Gravity Trap" riffles have done their job!

EIGHT. Dip a small amount of water into the pan and tip it backward, washing the small amount of concentrates to the bottom. Swirl the water in a light circular motion causing the contents to spread out gradually. This permits the best visual identification. The larger gold flakes, garnets, sapphires, etc. (anything large enough to be picked up with small tweezers), should now be removed. Actually, the most minute pieces may be removed with pointed tweezers if you wish to expend the effort. Place your precious metals or gems into a small bottle for safekeeping and transporting home. They will show better with a small amount of water added to the bottle. Generally, most panning books and instructions now say to drop a small

#7                          #8

amount of mercury into the material that cannot be picked up
with tweezers. Actually, unless this amalgamation operation is
on a large scale you could never gather enough in this manner
to fill a tooth. Also, once you have put mercury on gold it des-
troys the gold's color, makes it almost impossible to sell (except
to brokers in large amounts), and generally is not worth the
effort on so small an amount. However, do not become discour-
aged and dump it back just yet. The "Gravity Trap" pan has
one more important function that cannot be duplicated by pans
of any other type or design. (These pans are used extensively in
the western gold mining states by professionals for this very
same function.) During the panning actions described through
Step Seven, you continually kept the sharp 90-degree riffles in
the downward or 12:00 position. This prevented any escape of
gold, but now the pan should be used in a different manner in
order to separate the tiny amount of leftover concentrates.

   With one hand grasp the pan by the rim where the riffles
are located and keep the pan in a level position. The "Gravity
Trap" pan actually has another trap; it is the continuous rounded trap formed by the recessed pan bottom. The trap is more
efficient for handling tiny amounts of concentrates. The circular trap contains the same 90-degree design as the three outer

Author demonstrates the ease with which the "Gravity Trap" gold pan's circular bottom trap separates the black sand concentrates and retains even the smallest, microscopic particles of gold. Be sure to use a slight, gentle circular motion for this final operation. This separating process would be almost impossible to do without the specially finished surface of the plastic "Gravity Trap" gold pan.

rim riffles and will perform the same marvelous trapping function. Place a small quantity of water into the pan, and carefully agitate the small amount of concentrates against this bottom trap. Slowly tilt the pan downward, (keeping the riffles up this time), using a side-to-side motion with a more pronounced circular swirl. When you get the action perfectly right, you will notice, that the small grains of black sand will "climb" up and out on the smooth side (opposite the riffle side) of the pan. You may also notice some of the fine flour gold doing likewise. Adjust your gentle shaking motion until *only* the black sand has climbed out of the bottom trap. Stop the shaking motion; dip the edge of the pan under water just enough to reach the black sand lying on the side of the pan; withdraw the pan gently from the water. Do this several times until the black sand has washed away. If you do this carefully you will notice *all* of the small microscopic flakes of gold will continue to stay, or hold longer, onto the plastic surface while the black sand is working itself slowly forward and off. This is one of the tremendous advantages of Garrett's specially finished plastic surface over steel or slick, greasy-appearing plastic.

You will also quickly understand why this particular shade

24

of green was chosen. All of the microscopic particles of gold show plainly; otherwise they would hardly be visible, even under powerful magnification. Darker shades of green or *black* would not permit such easy visual identification. Continue this practice, and you will be able to separate the concentrates completely, leaving only the last fine piece of flour gold. This gold saving feat is performed every day by experienced panners. And now, you can do it, too!

If you are an experienced gold panner to begin with, and have completed these instructions, you have seen the definite advantages of the "Gravity Trap" pan for cleanups, pot holing and snipping. It is a true and modern time-saving tool that will speed up the professional's panning time by approximately three times as much or more. If you are a beginner, you have gained confidence from having the advantages of the sharp 90-degree riffle traps to protect you while learning. Professional prospectors throughout the world have acclaimed it as by far the *fastest* and *surest* gold saver except the old trusty sluice box.

There could be no greater testimonial. That is why it is protected by trademark registration and has been awarded United States Patent Number 4,162,969.

Mexican prospector, David Medrano, Roy Lagal, and Charles Garrett pan silver 350 miles south of El Paso, Texas, in the state of Chihuahua, Mexico. This fabled region is rich in silver, gold, and precious gems. The introduction of the "Gravity Trap" Gold Pan into this region caused quite a stir among Mexican prospectors who had for ages used their far less efficient, hand made wooden pans.

25

CHAPTER IV

# Dry Panning Instructions

INTRODUCTION. Dry panning has been debunked, maligned and distorted so many times it is hard to get at the truth. Quite frankly, only large scale mining operations using sophisticated equipment are successful in recovering fine gold by dry methods in quantities large enough to make it profitable. However, there are many individual prospectors who use the small type of dry washer. These are easily portable and are either hand-operated or drive by a small motor. They are used mainly to test an area to see if it would warrant more exploration. Many prospectors use them on weekend outings, but it would be quite difficult to make a living using one. Those who enjoy searching the dry desert areas, either as a hobby or for actual prospecting explorations, will find that the Garrett "Gravity Trap" pan with its portability and low cost advantages will also work perfectly as a dry washer, but on a rather small scale. I once had the good fortune to be seated, unobserved, at the rear of an auditorium during a lengthy discussion on gold pans and dry panning methods. The speaker was a nationally-known writer and dealer in mining supplies, but he was not too widely-experienced in the mining field, except perhaps in his own locality. He made the remark, "The Garrett 'Gravity Trap' gold pan does not in the least make dry panning possible." As I did not wish to embarrass him in public, I made no comment, and did not offer to show him how simple and easy the pan is to use. However, I am still a firm believer in total honesty regarding facts and equipment, and I will keep my mouth shut when it comes to something I know nothing about. As George Massie, President of Gold Prospectors Association of America, puts it, "When you stand in front of two or three hundred experienced prospectors you had better know your business. A few may just insist on your showing them 'how,' using their own equipment, or invite you to perform the same demonstration using sand and gravel supplied from their own 'diggin's'." You can see this is no place for showboaters and fakers who use a carnival atmosphere to promote products. Any type of mining equipment will eventually have to stand on its own merits, and experienced counsellors

26

Author using metal detector in dry river bed to locate nuggets which can be recovered immediately by digging, or ore pockets and vein structures which can be investigated and analyzed on the spot by panning samples taken from the detected hot spots (see Chapter V). Electronic prospecting has become extremely popular now that VLF/TR ground canceling detectors are available and the value of gold and silver has skyrocketed.

27

Author pouring concentrates from dry panning into coffee can for later wet panning separation at home.

will always stress slow, but positive results, *especially* when first using new methods or tools.

The dry washer uses a table constructed much like the ordinary sluice box. It is oblong, approximately six to twelve inches wide, and has a series of riffles to trap the gold. The riffles are placed in an upright position at a 90-degree angle and at right angles to the long box or trough. The dry gravel or sand (it must be completely dry) is fed slowly into the trough which is placed on a slight downward slope. The trough or box is then shaken, or vibrated by means of a small hand crank or motor, causing the material to slip slowly over the 90-degree riffles. The heavier gold settles to the bottom of the trough and is, in turn, stopped by the upright riffles. Continued shaking, vibration and forced air cause the lighter sand and gravel to travel downhill, slip over the top of the sharp riffles, and then off onto a tailing pile. The heavier gold and black sand concentrates remain securely trapped behind or in front of the upright 90-degree riffle.

What you have just read is also an exact description of the operational function of the famous Garrett "Gravity Trap" pan. The Garrett pan uses the SAME sharp riffles, constructed in the plastic at a true 90 degrees, and performs EXACTLY the same function. The portable dry washer is oblong, and is shaken or vibrated by mechanical means. The Garrett "Gravity Trap" pan is round and is shaken or vibrated by hand. The drywasher will process more gravel or sand, but is heavier and harder to transport, plus it costs much more. The "Gravity Trap" pan will not process nearly so much dry material, but it is extremely lightweight, small, and easy to transport, plus the cost is almost nothing in comparison. The results, or amount of recovery, from either device depend entirely upon the expertise and methods used by the operator. Now you can understand how ridiculous the statement sounded that was made by the unknowledgeable dealer of mining supplies.

In wet panning it was stressed that the material MUST ALWAYS be in a liquid or suspended state; otherwise, the gold will NOT settle down through the damp or merely wet sand. The opposite holds true when using the dry method of recovery. The sand or gravel must be *completely* dry. It cannot be even *slightly* damp for the gold will not settle down through the dense material without much agitating and the gold must be in the loose suspension of the dry sand or gravel. Dry panning is rather difficult when used as a method of recovery on fine gold. If the operator has the patience and employs the correct methods, it *can* be accomplished while using the "Gravity Trap" pan. Of course, when the gold is heavier and in larger pieces, it is *much* easier and more practical. It is only mentioned in passing that it *is* entirely possible to pan light or flake gold. Experienced gold panners have dry panned for many years with only conventional pans, though this requires much experience, expertise and time. The "Gravity Trap" pan is actually a miniature dry washer with the same riffle design but constructed in a round shape. It is operated by hand-controlled power, the same as the small portable drywashers are. It remains only for the prospector to put its capability to proper use.

ONE. Make sure any material you obtain is completely dry. The biggest mistake in dry panning is filling the pan TOO full. Fill your pan to approximately one-third to one-half full on your first attempt. You may then progress to approximately one-half to two-thirds full. Follow the same procedures in locating your gravel or panning material from approximately the same likely spots where you obtained it for wet panning. Of course, you will NOT be able to take the gravel from beneath the water, but if the stream bed is dry you should shovel away the loose gravel or overburden, and try to get as close to bed-

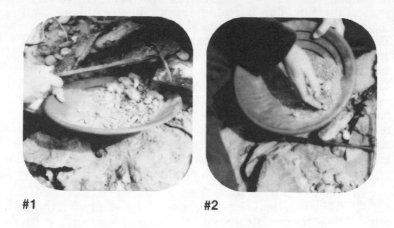

#1                    #2

rock as possible. Use a small bar, pick, screwdriver, rock hammer, or whatever tool is handy. Dig as deeply into the crevices as you can and, if possible, use a small whisk broom to sweep the contents onto a shovel, small garden trowel, or whatever digging tool you may employ. Continue filling the pan until you reach the desired level of contents.

If you are in a desert location it is sometimes possible to use a metal/mineral detector to locate the heavier concentrates of black sand pockets. These pockets do not always contain gold, but the black sand and the gold tend to become trapped in the same locations because of their heavier weight and the ever-present law of gravity. Otherwise, you may prospect the area by testing the bottom of drywashes and natural-appearing gravity traps that nature provided. Gravel deposits occur far out in the desert and far up on some mountain tops. These may be from glacier dropoffs or ancient river bed deposits. Many times such areas are rich in gold, but have never been tested by the old-time prospectors due to the absence of water for panning. Your "Gravity Trap" pan is light and fast to use, so keep these areas constantly in mind as they may be checked or tested quick easily and quickly. You will many times discover

30

gold or other metals in *just plain old dry dirt*. These metals or gems are generally washed down from some higher vein or decomposed ore pocket. Assuming you have now obtained some gravel that may contain gold, other precious metals, or perhaps semi-precious gem stones, you may now proceed to the next step.

TWO. If it has been impossible for you to go into the field and you wish to gain additional experience and confidence by simulated dry panning, place some small birdshot (BB's) into any type of dry road gravel, sand, plain dirt, or whatever is at hand. If you use real gold or other valuable metals it would be advisable to let the tailings or discards drop onto a small canvas, piece of tin or other metal container, or, better yet, another gold pan. Then you may develop speed without fear of irretrievable loss. Simply pan the material from one pan back into the other pan until you gain the necessary expertise and speed. Dropping a few small BB's or other types of small heavy metal onto the top of the dry gravel will quickly teach you the first necessary step.

Set the pan down on a flat firm surface; plunge your hands into the dry material; and stir the contents briskly and thoroughly, completely to the bottom of the pan. Notice this caused the BB's or other small, but heavy objects to settle downward toward the bottom. Otherwise, they might have remained in the upper layers of the gravel even after much shaking. Start picking out the larger rocks and gravel. Forcefully tap them together to loosen any gold that may be clinging to their surfaces. Continue this discarding action while watching closely for any large nugget or gemstone that you might discard. You may give the pan a few vigorous shakes, either side-to-side, up or down, in a circular motion, or otherwise. At this point, the type of agitation does not have any bearing other than that the vibration does help to settle the smaller, but heavier pieces of material. The main procedure through this step is to continue to stir the contents thoroughly by hand and continue to discard the larger pebbles as this lessens the weight and compactness of material so it will loosen when shaken later.

You may carefully rake this larger material and worthless debris over the edge (watch for valuable nuggets or gems), provided you allow the small sand to sift through your fingers back *into* the pan. There is almost NO chance of your losing any heavier pieces of gold (or practice BB's) during this step. Be sure all the raking off is done across the gravity traps because to do so will insure that the heavier material has a chance to drop down and become trapped in the same method as it did in the small, portable drywasher. It is best to continue cleaning and discarding all the rocks, small pebbles and debris during this step until only a small amount of concentrated light gravel and sand remains. This is much faster and easier done by hand during this stage, and there is considerably less chance of loss by this method than there would be if you attempted to begin the vibrating and spilling off of the lighter material before the pan's contents became sufficiently lightened or completely loosened. Continued experimentations of this quick and easy method of raking the dry material over the "Gravity Trap" riffles will quickly give you complete confidence that it is almost *impossible* to get the smaller and heavier pieces of metal out of the pan. Of course, it *could* happen if you became excessively careless and paid absolutely no attention to the facts of gravity. A small, portable drywasher must have the material screened down to a particular size "mesh" before it will recover properly. This is actually what you are accomplishing with the finger sifting method, though, of course, much more crudely. You now expect the "Gravity Trap" gold pan to perform efficiently, but under much *harsher circumstances*. With proper attention to handling procedures, it will do exactly that, for it is actually a miniature drywasher in circular form. You should have approximately one to two cups of material left in the pan and be ready for the next step.

THREE. Next, grasp edge of pan firmly with one hand and slowly tilt pan downward, making certain the sharp 90-degree riffle traps are in the lower portion of pan. Use your free hand to bump the upper edge of pan sharply. This sharp, continuous bumping action causes the heavier gold (or BB's) to settle downward through the dry sand and small gravel, finally coming to rest on the bottom. The heavier concentrates will also crawl uphill toward the side being bumped. You must slowly increase the downward tilt of the pan, causing the lighter material to slip gradually down and off over the lower edge of the pan. Tilting the pan downward too *quickly* does not give the heavier gold time to settle completely down through the top sand and gravel. Tilting the pan downward too *slowly* allows the gold to settle completely and then crawl *upward* and back toward you. You will notice the concentrates becoming visible and then starting to fall back over the top material. They then begin to travel downward again, but they are no longer on the bottom. The sharp 90-degree riffle traps have been prevented

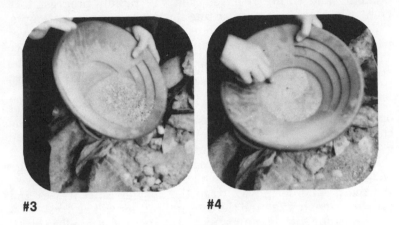

**#3**                    **#4**

from performing their purpose. The large portable drywasher is set at a downward tilt, and you provide the vibration which causes the lighter material to slip over the riffle traps. The action is the same as the "Gravity Trap" pan. The riffles are the same, but YOU must set the slope while continuing to provide the vibrating action with your hand. This does take some bit of coordination between your two hands, but after one or two practice sessions it becomes so easy that a small child can perform dry panning with complete confidence *and exceptional speed.*

If you become unsure of yourself, simply tilt the pan upward, regroup the material back to the bottom and start all over again. Sometimes you can spot the black sand or concentrates that have become settled or trapped in the sharp riffles as you bring the material back to the bottom. This will generally give you greater confidence to increase your speed. Do not be afraid to bump sharply and firmly or tilt the pan downward. The "Gravity Trap" riffles will *stop* the heavier gold and practice BB's. You should do this TOO FAST at least once or twice. Then, when you do it TOO SLOWLY, you will easily recognize what is happening. With continued practice of the amount of bumping and tilting required, you will rapidly progress to a point where you can recover fine flour gold on some attempts. This is, quite frankly, sometimes impossible to do even in wet panning, depending upon the fine or lighter gold. The "Gravity Trap" pan will serve you well, both in the desert and in the streams. You cannot cook in it, but you sure don't have to burn it!

You can use mercury (if necessary) and acid in either a wet or dry combination. You can take the pan to the beach, and the children can dry pan for lost coins (even a small coin will trap quickly in the riffles). You can use it to pan for gems, although this does require more careful panning methods as the average weight of gem material is much less than that of gold; however, the sharp riffle design will trap the heavier concentrates and give you time to examine the contents, either wet or dry.

Continue the bumping and slipping off procedure until only a small amount of concentrates remains. DO NOT ATTEMPT TO PAN THE DRY CONCENTRATES DOWN AS CLEANLY AS YOU DID IN THE WET PANNING METHOD. The "Gravity Trap" pan has accomplished its purpose, and you

Author gently blowing the lighter sand away from the heavier gold particles.

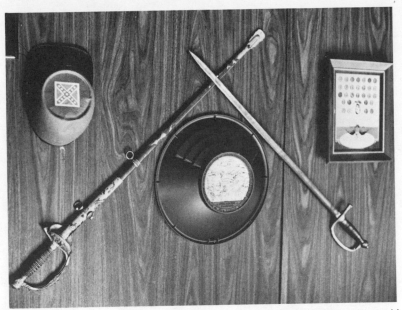

The Garrett "Gravity Trap" gold pan is the official pan selected for many gold panning championship contests. It is used extensively by clubs and organizations for gifts and prize awards.

should have only one-fourth or one-half cupful of pure concentrates left.

FOUR. Carefully inspect this small amount of dry concentrates for gold nuggets, gold flakes, valuable metal or mineral specimens, and, of course, remember the semi-precious gems. This is best accomplished by spreading the concentrates in a thin pattern over the bottom of the pan. If you use caution it is possible to blow gently across the material to uncover some of the smaller pieces of gold and make them visible to the naked eye. This is one of the times when a magnifying glass will be useful. The magnifier will permit close inspection of the concentrates and perhaps save you the trouble of carrying home worthless iron sand. There is no practical method of reducing the concentrates down any cleaner without water, so it is best to dump them into another container and take them home for later inspection and wet panning procedures. There is no question that dry panning and dry washing methods recover only the heavier gold particles; otherwise, there would be thousands of mining operations all over the desert areas recovering the fine, light gold. There are many such areas that could be worked profitably if water were present to conduct sluicing operations.

Wet recovery is the easiest and most profitable method, but lack of water prevents this. Many deep wells are being drilled in desert areas in an attempt to overcome this handicap. Present dry washing operations being conducted are on a large-scale basis, and are generally conducted only in the richer areas. There are countless dry areas and even entire states that remain relatively unexplored as to mineral content. The average everyday prospector is venturing forth in greater numbers than ever before, and new discoveries are sure to come forth.

# CHAPTER V

# The Most Likely Places for You to Find Gold

## IN WATER

The presence of water certainly does not indicate the presence of GOLD, but it does make the search for and identification of it easier. PANNING is the quickest, most practical way to separate small amounts of lighter gravel and debris from the heavier elements and metals . . . hopefully, GOLD. Instructing one on where to find gold is like attempting to teach one how to become a millionaire. Why isn't the writer one? However, by describing where gold is or is NOT likely to be found, it is possible to save the novice (and sometimes the professional) many fruitless attempts at recovery. Experience and years of prospecting have enlightened some of us considerably, but still the irrefutable fact remains, GOLD IS WHERE YOU FIND IT.

Gold is not likely to be found in old dredge tailings, though there are exceptions where the dredge operator was not aware of unusually large nuggets and lost them in the tailings or discards. The dredge ripped up the bedrock by large buckets designed to remove the first foot or so of material, and there are no cracks or fissures filled with gold left beneath the loose tailings. Also unlikely as sources of gold are areas that were worked extensively by early-day miners. They seldom missed any of the small pockets that many look for, particularly in the rich placer zones. Of course, a FEW spots were missed, but generally you will never have the time nor equipment to find them. If the small creek or river abounds with loose material, gravel, etc., and the area shows evidence of early-day activities, it is usually safe to assume the ground has been turned over or sluiced by many succeeding generations of miners. These worked out areas produce only light flour gold.

Confine your searching to places where it is possible to locate small isolated spots that have been relatively undisturbed. Gravel that has never been worked will be tight and hard packed. Search carefully by digging underneath the overburden to find if waterworn rocks are present (river gravel). Certain deposits will contain different layers of gravel that were deposited many thousands of years apart. Test the deposit at different depths as gold is sometimes deposited far above bedrock. This, though,

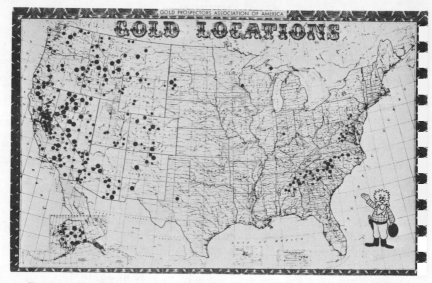

This map is included only as a guide to U.S. gold producing areas. See the appendix, dealer listing, and recommended books for sources of information (state bureaus of mines and geology, etc.) about gold locations in the U. S., Canada, Australia, and other countries.

is not often the case because gold is heavy and quickly sinks, working its way down into the finest cracks and fissures before becoming trapped. However, many rich and profitable gravel deposits are passed over or abandoned in the mistaken belief that gold is found only on bedrock.

Searches conducted in flowing water are difficult, but not impossible. Some streams contain only alluvial gold that is washed down each year during high water. This type of gold is found throughout the loose gravel with the largest concentrations being stopped by hard packed gravel or bedrock. Of course, natural traps, such as large boulders, tree roots, moss, slower sections of water flow, inside bends, etc., will probably contain the most gold. Dredging is the fastest way to test when exploring beneath flowing water, but it *is* possible to test with shovel and pan. Use your shovel to rake or remove the loose top gravel. Try to get your material from the firmly packed bottom or on bedrock itself. Gently bring the shovel up out of the water, depositing the gravel into your pan. The water will tend to rob the shovel when this is attempted so move slowly and carefully. Many dredgers test by the shovel method before bringing their dredge to a specific area. If you can actually see the bedrock it may be possible to use a prybar and loosen some of the bedrock to expose gravel and gold that has been trapped for years. Here, the small suction type dredge is practically the only sure and useful equipment. Whether using shovel or dredge underwater, ALWAYS try to loosen the bedrock and then thoroughly clean even the smallest cracks. Once you have disturbed hard packed gravel the gold will sink quickly to the bottom, making recovery more difficult.

Use the illustrated map as a helpful guide. Do not depend on gold's being at any given spot. Check the outline of the river or stream course carefully. The channel may have changed over the years, and the older channel may contain the richest deposits. Try imagining where the stream flowed in past years — the curves or bends, where the water was forced to move fast, where it had a chance to slow down, etc. Gold will settle wherever the water flows most slowly; it will whip around and become trapped in rough sections of bedrock; but seldom is it found in smooth or waterworn sections, especially where the current is fast. Waterfalls and potholes seldom produce because the fast water and rocks create a mill that grinds the gold to dust and returns it to the water flow. Look for feeder creeks and isolated spots where the old-timers could not get water for sluicing. Use your shovel to dig beneath the loose gravel. The major fault of the weekend prospector's method is that he simply scoops up loose gravel with his gold pan, expecting it to contain gold. It rarely does. Dig test holes away from the stream bed, where you suspect the original channel was. You will quickly identify the channel by the presence of waterworn gravel.

## IN DRY AREAS

The absence of water does not prohibit but it certainly does complicate the *location* and recovery of gold. The precious metal is hard to recognize in small flake form and in ore (rock) unless wet. Small flakes and tiny nuggets can be recovered by dry panning or dry washing methods, yet they are more difficult to see unless wet or clean from small dust. Old prospectors who worked the pocket country used a pail of water in which to dip the ore while sorting out the high grade. Many times this procedure is impossible; sometimes it is unnecessary. However, the fact remains that water helps the identification process considerably. Unless gold, especially the placer form, was discovered accidentally in the dry areas, most searching was confined to the location of veins (hardrock composition). The working of rich placer areas where water is not available is still in its infancy. The crushing and milling of ore depends on water for separation of the concentrates. There are other methods, but use of water is the most economical and easiest. This presents an important fact: because of the absence of water, MILLIONS OF DOLLARS LIE IN PLAIN SIGHT in undiscovered and unworked dry mineral zones.

A few areas of search are deemed better to avoid. Light, windblown sand seldom contains gold. Even fine flour gold is usually not present in paying quantities. In different states certain rock formations and mineral zones are generally barren. These can be identified by the study of local geological reports. Black loam soil in farming areas is almost always barren of gold, but does contain some small amounts of magnetic iron oxides. It is not wise to rule out *too* many areas since the old cliché still holds true . . . GOLD IS WHERE YOU FIND IT.

Searches for gold in placer or alluvial form can be conducted by various methods. The most practical would be to use a small dry washer or gold pan designed for dry panning to spot test an area, saving the heavier concentrates for later separation by wet panning. Wet panning is more sure than dry panning because, without liquid to produce a state of suspension, it is difficult to save light gold. Rarely is gold large enough in dry placer form to be visible with the naked eye, except in nugget form. This fact makes the use of metal/mineral detectors impractical, except for the locating of large nuggets or black sand pockets that MIGHT possibly contain gold. Also, the fine gold is usually scattered and not in sufficient amounts to respond to electronic detection. Dig beneath the overburden whenever possible, especially in ancient riverbed areas. Attempt to reach bedrock, pry loose the surface whenever possible, and use a small screwdriver or ice pick to clean the smallest cracks. Use a small whisk broom to sweep the finest dust into your pan. You can transport the dry material to water for separation or, with practice, you can learn to pan down to the heavier concentrates by dry methods. Spot-check any type of desert streambed, low area — anywhere you think gravity could have placed the heavier concentrates.

The search for glacial deposits and bench placers will differ from the search for lighter gold. In this case it is possible some large nuggets may be present. The visible recognition of waterworn rocks quickly identifies these deposits as being placed by water action and later perhaps moved or displaced by nature. You may follow closely the same instructions and recovery methods used in water. Attempt to reach bedrock when possible, taking care to test the gravel thoroughly at different depths; follow dry panning instructions and save the heaviest concentrates. Now that there is a possibility to find nuggets sufficiently large to respond to electronic detection, your chances of success with a metal detector are much increased. Recent improvements and the introduction of mineral-free operation metal detector types have made the recovery of large gold nuggets simple enough for even the smallest child. All that is required is that you use the correct type of detector and that nuggets be present in sufficient size and not too deep to respond to electronic detection. Dry areas provide the most practical situations for metal detectors, and there are vast, unlimited, easy-to-reach mineral zones that are known to contain gold.

The map illustration provides a perfect example of nature and the forces of gravity. Unless trapped or stopped by some natural or man-made obstruction, gold continues to work its way forever downward, eventually into the depths of the oceans. As this action takes place, the gold nuggets continue to be worn, battered and ground until they become pure dust. The knowledge of this gravity force will enable you to follow many forms of placer gold to their sources. Seldom is there a sufficient amount of fine gold scattered over any type of terrain to make recovery profitable. Where conditions permit, however, fine gold may be followed to its point of entry on the surface. Hard work and much panning is required for pocket location. Tracing of fine gold which is being gradually washed from a glacial deposit is hardly ever practical. However, tracing gold or float from a vein can be both practical and profitable, especially with metal/mineral detectors. High grade specimens are relatively easy to locate with a mineral-free operation type of detector, provided the specimen contains a sufficient amount of metallics to be highly conductive, a factor which depends on the search area and the richness of the ore. Actual location of the pocket or vein structure can be accomplished with the correct tools: a gold pan designed for both wet or dry panning and a mineral-free operation type of detector or a BFO type with small searchcoil (5-inch or smaller). There are unlimited opportunities in dry desert areas. The gold has simply lain there in plain sight over many millions of years. It will continue to do so until some enterprising modern-day prospector takes advantage of the latest detection and recovery methods.

If the area where you live has not been prospected before, remember that GOLD has been found in all fifty states. Play

41

your hunches. Our forefathers did. Many found gold in paying quantities; some made fortunes. Whether you find gold is of little consequence, for the shovel and faithful gold pan will enrich your life by knowledge gained and provide you with the most interesting hobby you can pursue.

# CHAPTER VI

## Gold Panning and the Metal / Mineral Detector

Is the metal/mineral detector an aid to using the gold pan? Yes, the metal detector can definitely be of assistance in locating pockets of black sand, and it may also be used to locate large nuggets of pure gold that are of a conductive nature. You will almost always have to make use of the trusty gold pan to pan or sort through rubble of rocks and sand to locate the small metallic object that responded to the metal detector. Remember, the target will sometimes be only a spent bullet or other metallic object that has become placed either by nature or by man into the stream or dry wash. In either case you may have no way of knowing until you use the gold pan to settle the heavier concentrates and separate the lighter material.

The use of the plastic gold pan is almost a "must" for this procedure. You would "detect" a metal pan if you attempted to

Boy! Aren't you glad I didn't forget the detector?

43

The plastic gold pan and metal detector go hand-in-hand. The "Gravity Trap" gold pan is recommended because its sharp 90-degree riffle design is practical for both wet or dry panning. It is constructed of a non-conductive material. When a metallic detector signal, however faint, is received, scoop out the sand and gravel at that spot and place it in the pan. If no detector signal is heard when checking the contents of the pan, dump the pan, scoop deeper, and again check the contents of the pan.

use your detector over the rocks and sand you placed in the pan. By use of plastic pans you can quickly determine if you have placed the metallic targets into the pan on your first attempt. If not, you can dump the pan and dig deeper or more carefully on your next attempt.

Location of black sand deposits that may contain gold can best be accomplished with a BFO type detector. Due to the continuous sound factor and the availability of either "mineral" or "metal" tuning, the BFO is well suited for the combination searching of BOTH nuggets *and* black sand deposits in one single operation. Because of the short tuning range of the standard coin hunting TR or IB detector, it is almost totally impossible to use that type detector in heavily mineralized areas. Correct application of the BFO for this type operation will help locate and properly identify iron stringers and nuggets. However, remember if you are searching for large nuggets ONLY, and the location is in a creek bed that abounds in rocks of high mineral content, the specially constructed VLF type detector will definitely be the best to use. With the VLF type you lose the ability to detect mineral pockets, but gain the advantage of "super" sensitivity on small metallic objects (nuggets). Remember, however, that under certain conditions any VLF type will respond positively to "out of place" rocks that contain a much greater magnetic mineral concentration than the river bed. Some brands of VLF type detectors can identify these "out of place" rocks easily. Check the manufacturer's detector brochures to be certain. For a complete explanation of metal/mineral detectors write to Garrett Electronics, Dept. GP2, 2814 National Drive, Garland, Texas 75041, for a free copy of Charles Garrett's *TREASURE HUNTING SECRETS.*

One note of caution may be given here. Always make certain the detector searchcoil is fully, one-hundred-percent shielded when attempting to nugget shoot in running water. It matters not whether the unit is BFO or some type of VLF. If the searchcoil does NOT employ a full Faraday shield it will be practically useless when employed in running water. So ALWAYS insist that any nugget hunting detector have a FULL FARADAY SHIELD, regardless of type. There have been many, many disappointed operators and failures over the years due to this overlooked but very important item. This need not be attributed to the detector's inefficiency, but just to the manufacturer's failure to employ a full Faraday-shielded searchcoil.

Regardless of the type detector you own or are using, tune it according to the manufacturer's recommendations. Select

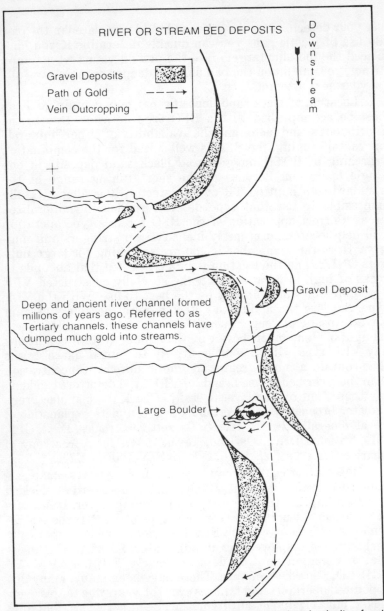

## RIVER OR STREAM BED DEPOSITS

Downstream

**Gravel Deposits**

**Path of Gold** - - - →

**Vein Outcropping** +

← Gravel Deposit

Deep and ancient river channel formed millions of years ago. Referred to as Tertiary channels. these channels have dumped much gold into streams.

Large Boulder →

Regardless of the appearance of the present river channel and velocity of water flow, many changes may have taken place over the millions of years. River bends, current changes, amount of water flow and turbulence may have moved or displaced gold into unsuspected areas. Note the dotted lines that MAY indicate what *could* have happened. *It pays to look!*

your stream bed, either wet or dry; proceed in either direction, up or down; and pay close attention to the faint signals as the nuggets are generally rather small or may be deep. When you receive a target response, lay your detector down if possible, attempt to slip a shovel or like tool under the spot where the signal occurred. Be extremely careful as the small but heavier metallic objects always tend to sink farther down into the rocks. Place the small amount of gravel or sand you recover into your plastic gold pan and quickly check the material with your detector. If the target is in the pan the detector will respond. If there is no response dump the contents of the pan, and attempt to get under the object on the next try. After a small amount of practice you will become quite proficient at this and will save considerable time by inventing special tools for the particular job.

If you are searching dry wash or old placer diggings the procedures will be the same. The only difference is that the object is easier to locate.

When searching old dredge tailings, you may lose many "targets" on your first attempt to dig down and recover them. Once these targets are disturbed they tend to drop on down through the dredge tailings and sometimes become impossible to re-locate. In searching dredge tailings the specially-constructed, very low frequency (VLF), mineral-free-operation type detector is practically the only detector that will produce satisfactory results. In the years to come this type of searching will be one of the most lucrative, productive fields in the metal detector field. There are many recent improvements in metal detectors, and when this fact becomes public knowledge there will be another gold rush that, who knows, might equal that of the '49'ers. The advantage of the modern searcher is that someone else has done the digging and missed some of the goodies!

CHAPTER VII

# An Introduction to Prospecting with the Metal/Mineral Detector

While it is impossible to guarantee success in the prospecting field, if you follow three basic rules you can be almost certain to find a quantity of *GOLD* or other precious metal in some form.

FIRST: Choose the correct TYPE of detector for prospecting. This does not necessarily mean some particular brand name or model. There are many different models manufactured in each detector TYPE, and they vary greatly in price. Various detector types are: Transmitter Receiver (TR); Induction Balance (IB); Radio Frequency (RF); Pulse Induction (Pulsedec and Pimdec); Discriminators (both TR and BFO); Beat Frequency Oscillator (BFO); and the Very Low Frequency (VLF), with such trade names as GEB, MPD, TGC, MF, GCD, GAD, RM, Magnum, etc. Frequently there will be additions to this listing, but basically they will fall under these TYPES and are merely "brand" names with the manufacturer calling attention to some particular feature or operating characteristic.

The Very Low Frequency (VLF) ground canceling detector and the Beat Frequency Oscillator (BFO) are best suited for analyzing small conductive ore specimens; high-grading old mine dumps; searching inside mines for overlooked, but rich, conductive or non-conductive pockets. They excel in the seeking of small stringers or pockets of magnetic black sand ($Fe_3O_4$). The BFO and certain VLF detectors are the only types capable of identifying metal *versus* mineral in small marginal amounts 100%-correctly. They will also respond to small conductive flakes of gold when used in bench tests. You should conduct a test of this kind when considering the purchase of a BFO or VLF detector for this type of prospecting. Choose a model with HIGH sensitivity, perfect stability, and one that incorporates a full range discrimination control. This control permits you to adjust the detector for operation in the discriminating mode for treasure hunting or ore sample identifying when prospecting.

Remember to compare makes and models using the SAME COIL SIZE. Coil sizes are very important. The BFO detector, to be capable of performing perfectly regardless of the situation, should be able to accommodate a full complement of search loops, ranging in size from small nugget probes to the larger coils. The VLF types, when correctly designed, can perform almost all prospecting functions, and do them well, with a 7 to 8 inch size searchcoil. Larger sizes, such as 10 to 14 inch, perform well when searching for large nuggets, deep ore veins, *etc*. The searchcoils should be fully 100% Faraday-shielded. This is *very* important when you search inside highly mineralized mines, caves, or in wet grass and weeds. The detector should employ a WIDE manual tuning range and be extremely stable with only minimal drift.

Small natural gold nuggets will be detected as good on the audio portion of the BFO, but will be rejected as bad on the discriminating meter. This presents no problem as long as you fully understand what is occurring when using a twin-circuit discriminating detector for metal *versus* mineral identification. Some advanced BFO detectors that employ the discriminating circuit as an aid to coin hunting also make use of an external switch whereby you may change from the discriminating mode to the non-discriminating mode. The non-discriminating mode is the most practical when searching for precious metal and minerals in their natural state.

The author uses both the BFO and VLF type detectors in mineralized stream beds. Depending on the amount of mineralization present, one might produce better results than the other. However, the VLF type should never be used in highly mineralized or trash-infested (iron junk) stream beds without the all-purpose BFO on hand as a back-up unit.

You will experience some difficulty when attempting to use the BFO for nugget hunting in a few rocky stream beds, especially those that contain a high amount of mineralization (magnetic iron). The uneven surface and extreme negative effect of the black magnetic sand and rocks may make the recovery of small nuggets difficult.

Nugget searching in this type of terrain is best accomplished by the use of *specialized* detectors featuring high sensitivity with ability to completely balance out the effect of negative mineralization. Transmitter-receiver detectors designed and engineered in the EXTREME low frequency range (VLF types) will best accomplish this. These detectors will penetrate the magnetic black sand and generally have some type of ground zero or adjustment system that will almost completely eliminate the negative nature of the mineralization. Large gold nuggets can now be found among the mineralized rocks with ease. These specially constructed TR's are quite expensive and should NOT be confused with standard or common coin hunting TR (IB) detectors.

The standard type TR performs quite well on coins and is preferred by most operators for this purpose. Many conventional TR's also have auto-tuning or push-button operation. A few standard TR's using conventional configurations in their searchcoil construction are claimed to have complete metal/mineral identification capabilities. This is impossible due to the fact that the transmitter coil "sees" mineral as positive (metal) and the receiving coil "sees" mineral as negative, depending on which portion of the searchcoil comes into close contact with the specimen.

Numerous TR's and IB models use mineralized ground control adjustments, sensitivity control adjustments, etc. These all are, in effect, only GAIN control adjustments, and when the effect of the mineralization is reduced the sensitivity is also reduced. They do nothing to change the electromagnetic field pattern produced by the conventional configuration of the TR searchcoil commonly used in coin hunting detectors. These conventional TR (IB) models are extremely popular in the coin hunting field and produce the best results when used for this purpose. When true metal/mineral identification is desired, the BFO and certain VLF types designed for universal application must be used.

Frank Mellish from London, England, tries his hand at prospecting. Here he scans a seam from which gold has been recovered. Since the gold recovered from this vein was wire gold, Frank could have detected a mass pocket of the metal. Wire gold is not easily detectable unless its density is fairly great. Gold and silver nuggets, on the other hand, are readily detectable because of their solid nature.

A sensitivity test is recommended in selecting a BFO or VLF type for ore sample identification. Be sure when contemplating the purchase of any conventional TR (IB) type for prospecting that you perform a sensitivity test with the mineralized or ground adjustment control turned fully on. Place your small nuggets or metal target among mineralized rocks in a natural manner depicting the look of nature. The dismaying results that you achieve will probably enlighten you considerably.

Remember, ALL metal detectors find metal with some degree of success, but only the BFO and specially constructed TR detectors operating in the EXTREME low frequency range (one kHz to approximately 15 kHz) with a ground control to eliminate the blanket effect of mineralization will perform satisfactorily in the prospecting field. For those of you who wish to pursue this further, I recommend my book HOW TO TEST "Before Buying" DETECTOR FIELD GUIDE, published by Ram Publishing Company. Careful attention when choosing any TYPE of detector for any application or job will forestall many headaches and disappointments.

SECOND: You must have patience. Learn to understand your detector fully and become proficient in its use.

THIRD: You must learn where to start your search. No one finds gold or other precious metals where they do not exist. Stick to known, productive mining areas until you have become familiar with the telltale signs of mineral zones.

There are many things you can do with the correct TYPE of detector. It will open up completely new areas of action for the prospector. The thousands of modern-day prospectors who have been successful with the metal/mineral detector have done their RESEARCH and employed the virtues of WISDOM and PATIENCE.

# CHAPTER VIII

## *Rocks, Gems and Minerals and the Metal/Mineral Detector*

Without question, the most important and useful tool of the rockhound (besides his faithful rockhammer and patience) is the metal/mineral detector. Properly used it can be very rewarding, but it should not be used as the ultimate answer to the positive identification of all minerals and gems. Nothing will ever replace the knowledge gained from experience in the identification of semi-precious stones and gems. The metal/mineral detector should be used as an added accessory to the rockhound's field equipment. It will aid in the location of many conductive metallic specimens the human eye cannot distinguish or identify. There are many high grade specimens of different ores that can be overlooked on any given field trip.

Attempting to locate nuggets.

Saving the concentrates from a dredging operation. Dredge pictured is the new lightweight 2" Super Jet manufactured by OREGON GOLD DREDGE, LTD.

While the human eye cannot see inside an ore specimen, a good quality BFO and certain of the new VLF types can.

For identification purposes the metal/mineral detector defines "metal" as any metallic substance of a conductive nature in sufficient quantity to disturb the electromagnetic field of the searchcoil. Gold, silver, copper, and all the non-ferrous metals are just that — metals. Speaking of "mineral," we identify only minerals which respond to a metal detector. This is magnetic iron and iron oxide (the proper chemical content is $Fe_3O_4$). Refer to Chapter IX. What it all boils down to is: if the detector responds as "metallic," bring the target in for it contains conductive metal in some form. If the target responds as "mineral" this indicates only that the specimen contains *more* mineral than it does metal in any detectable form that would react to the detector. This means that for a few minutes' work you might come up with a high grade metallic sample that has been passed over for years by your fellow rockhounds.

Conduct bench tests to familiarize yourself with the responses produced by both metal and mineral. Use specimens with which you are already familiar as this will greatly aid in future identification. Refer to the bench tests conducted for the identification of ore samples. Basically, they will be the same. When conducting your field search, use the detector as an *aid*, not as a complete searching tool. In other words, test any likely-appearing rocks. This kind of testing and investigation will greatly increase your knowledge, and just may produce for you that valuable specimen we all desire.

Author using a metal/mineral detector to check a likely-looking piece of quartz for metallic (gold) content. This old river bed is in Montana, and this hole has produced many beautiful specimens of moss agate. A good quality BFO and certain of the new VLF types perform admirably in this ore sampling process. Check several manufacturers' brochures to determine which brand or brands are capable of performing this feat.

# CHAPTER IX

# Metal / Mineral Ore Sample
# Identification

METAL. Gold, silver, copper and other valued metals are natural non-ferrous metals and will respond to your detector as *metallic*, provided they are in a conductive form and in sufficient quantity to disturb the electromagnetic field of the searchcoil. Some high grade ores are in tellurides and other forms, and are NOT of sufficient conductivity to obtain a reading. You will find, however, that most free milling ores that contain high grade metal in the conductive form will produce good response.

MINERAL. For all practical purposes, the only mineral that the metal detector recognizes as "mineral" is $Fe_3O_4$, magnetic iron oxides (in other words, magnetic iron ore or magnetic black sand). This is extremely simple to test if the ore contains a predominance of either metal or mineral. If the specimen of ore contains *neither* metal nor mineral, you would receive no indication. There is a remote possibility the specimen may contain electrically *equal* and *exact* amounts of metal and mineral. In this case one would neutralize or balance out the effects of the other and NO indication would be received.

However, if the specimen reads as "mineral" this does not mean METAL is not present, only that there is a predominance of mineral. If the specimen reads as "metal" you can be certain the specimen contains metal in some conductive form in a quantity sufficient to disturb the searchcoil's electromagnetic field. This factor makes the metal/mineral detector the most important tool of today's successful prospector and miner.

## BENCH TESTING ORE SAMPLES

Place your detector prone on a table or bench, using one of the small searchcoils, preferably three to six inches. Tune the detector in the METAL mode of operation, adjusting the audio to a moderate beat or sound to enable you to hear faint signals more clearly. (Be sure to remove all metallic objects from your hand; *i.e.*, rings, watches, etc.) Quickly move an ore sample toward and away from the center of the searchcoil. Use the

Ore sample testing for conductive metal content can be accomplished only with correctly calibrated VLF/TR ground canceling detectors and with BFO detectors.

center of the coil as this area will give the best response.

If the sample contains NEITHER metal nor mineral, or has electrically equal amounts of both, you receive no response. If the sample has a predominance of metal in a detectable form, you will hear a slight beat and sound increase as the sample comes closer to the searchcoil. If you are using a detector model incorporating a sensitivity meter you will see a positive needle signal or movement to the right, indicating the presence of metals. If the sound dies or the beat slows when the sample approaches the coil, the sample contains a predominance of mineral or natural magnetic iron ($Fe_3O_4$). This does not mean the sample contains no metal, only that the sample contains MORE mineral than it does metal.

One of the advantages of using the BFO all-purpose detector to test ore samples is that it will indicate the presence of METALS in any conductive form. That is, you can be absolutely positive whether the specimen contains METALLIC substance in some form or other. The BFO will not react positively unless some form of conductive metallic substance disturbs the electromagnetic field.

Obtain samples of galena, silver, gold ore and just plain

rocks. By conducting your bench analysis you will become familiar with the type and amount of response to low grade and high grade ores. Also, many types of ore (tellurides) do NOT respond to metal detectors. Only those containing metal in the conductive form and in sufficient quantity to disturb the electromagnetic field respond to detectors.

For example, some large garnets will respond to mineral on a sensitive BFO because the garnet contains enough magnetic iron to respond. When checking samples that have responded as metal, you will generally notice a metallic appearance on the inside. When samples that appear metallic but respond as mineral are sawed or slabbed, you will generally notice a streak of magnetic iron on the inside. Since there was sufficient iron to override the small amount of metal, the sample responded as mineral.

Certain manufacturers' VLF types (as described in the manufacturers' brochures) will perform the tests discussed in this chapter. In fact, these detectors, which are equipped with especially designed searchcoils and have the correct type of discrimination adjustment control perform perfectly in most prospecting situations and should be seriously considered, particularly if you require extreme sensitivity (depth) and are interested in other phases of metal detection, such as coin hunting, cache (money) hunting, and relic (ghost town and battlefield) hunting.

# CHAPTER X

# *Searching Old Mine Dumps*

Working some of yesterday's forgotten ore dumps has become a very profitable pastime. Some large mining companies were after only certain minerals or metals. The human eye could not see inside the ore, and many good ore samples were discarded on the dump. The electronic metal detector can detect metals (of conductive form) inside almost any type of rock. Some dumps have been completely reworked for the minerals and metals that were left behind. Others are just awaiting the present-day prospector using a sensitive metal/mineral detector.

One of the greatest failings of the average treasure hunter who searches old mine dumps for high grade ore is to search the ore dump as one would search in usual treasure hunting. The searcher simply expects the detector to respond to small (BUT RICH) amounts of metals among all the rubble of extreme MINERAL concentration. It is not reasonable to expect any detector—no matter how sensitive—to detect small specimens of metal in all the jumble of rock that is generally very heavy with magnetic iron.

There are basically two different types of detectors that are successful in high-grading old mine dumps. The BFO and the specially constructed Very Low Frequency TR types operating in the one kilocycle-plus range. Standard coin hunting TR (IB) detectors are generally unsuccessful due to the high mineral (iron) content of the ore dump. They are hampered by their quick response factor which is so praised in the search for coins. The pulse inductance or Pulsedec instrument is almost completely unaffected by the natural magnetic iron content but does not "see" or respond to marginal ore samples even when in highly conductive form. Searching by many individuals who encounter failure can usually be attributed to an unwise choice in TYPE of detector, not price, model or brand name.

When using the BFO detector and you encounter a dump that may contain high grade ore specimens, lay your detector prone on the ground. Tune it in the metallic mode, using a small coil such as used in the bench analysis (3 or 6 inches). Pick a few small samples of rock from the pile to test for metal

59

SEARCHING OLD MINE DUMPS. Many mine dumps, rich in metals and minerals, are awaiting the present-day prospector who is using a sensitive metal detector. The BFO and certain of the new VLF types are recommended.

content. If, after a reasonable period of time, you do not find any metallic indications, move to another area of the dump. During the working period of the mine perhaps there was only a certain portion of the dump that could have received the tailings from the vein. The rest may be only debris from the mine's shafts and tunnels. Take rock or ore samples from many different locations, especially from the higher sections of the dump because this is where some of ALL the different pieces were dumped at one time or another. If after prolonged testing you do not recover at least a few metallic specimens, it may simply be a dump where the ore was of some type to which a metal/mineral detector could not respond. The ore may also have been of a very low grade composition of little value.

The best procedure is to do research and pick areas that produced the free-milling type of HIGH GRADE ore which will respond positively to the detector. The pocket country is ideal for this type of searching. Most old timers merely wet the rock in order to see the gold and took only the high grade ore, commonly called jewelry ore. Jewelry ore is worth much more than the weight in gold for specimens. "High grade" is in great demand today. I personally know many recreational miners who do quite well at this particular type of hunting. Someone else has already done the digging, and all the searcher has to do is grade or analyze the discarded rock left on top. A good quality BFO metal/mineral detector will enable you to do this easily, provided the metallic content is of a conductive type and rich enough to respond.

Use of the TR detectors that are engineered and constructed in the Very Low Frequency operating range will differ slightly from BFO operation. The VLF type may be turned or balanced to eliminate the effects of the blanket mineralization. This is extremely helpful in all search and recovery situations, BUT it still leaves one major fault of many of the VLF types. If the matrix or background mineralization is negative, and the VLF type is tuned accordingly, it may respond POSITIVE (as metal) on a piece of ore (rock) that contains an extra amount of mineral ($Fe_3O_4$). The only alternative is to purchase a VLF type that is designed to perform this feat and then carefully follow the manufacturer's instructions. You would then achieve true metal *versus* mineral identification. Failure to follow these instructions can easily result in causing your VLF type metal detector to respond erroneously on rocks with only high iron content.

As you can see each TYPE of detector has some advantage over other types when used for particular applications. Any hobbyist or professional miner who takes the time to study these instructions thoroughly will have no difficulty in finding many high-grade ore specimens left behind by a former miner. The science of electronic detecting of ore samples is in its infancy and with the advent of the new price of gold PLUS the demand for rare specimens, you can readily see that electronic detection has many advantages over visual searching. The BFO type detector and the VLF types described above definitely have the advantage in metal/mineral searching. You may use them to good advantage on old ore dumps.

Here again, I cannot stress the point enough that millions of dollars have lain unnoticed on both small and large ore dumps, in plain sight. Absolutely anyone with reasonable ambition can use the correct type of detector to excellent advantage on these discarded rock piles. You will be surprised at the valuable specimens you recover. Remember, a small rich specimen is worth many times its weight in gold or any other precious metal. Obtain one of the recommended detector types and check a few small mine dumps or prospect holes. I will wager my entire life-span of fifty-odd years, plus a reputation for honesty and "telling it like it is" that you will recover many small, but high grade specimens.

Follow my instructions on ore sampling and, if you are successful, pass the newly-gained knowledge on to a friend. There are enough discarded ore dumps to furnish everyone with many days of pleasurable activity and extra income for hundreds of years.

# CHAPTER XI

## *Weekend Gold Dredging with the Two-Inch Oregon "Super Jet"*

Underwater suction dredges are not new. They have been around quite some time, and have been used with varying degrees of success. However, as with all equipment, time will generate many improvements. Poor recovery rate and WEIGHT are the main drawbacks of most dredges. All, however, seem to be accepted by the recreational miner as the greatest tool available to facilitate the recovery of gold from shallow creeks, rivers, or areas that were impossible to work in the early gold rushes. Cracks in bedrock (underwater) are practically impossible to clean by any other method. The surface type gold dredge (the underwater models are seldom used any more) should be able to produce a reasonable recovery rate of fine gold and they are also easily portable. Portability seems to be the key to success. Much prospecting and moving from spot to spot until "color" is obtained in the sluice box is always necessary.

Claims of 90% to 100% recovery of fine gold are made by many dredge manufacturers. This is impossible. Some fine gold has a certain amount of natural oil (from the roots of grass, weeds and polluted water) and will simply float right on through *any* sluice box, especially in a surface suction dredge that is producing the large amount of water necessary to obtain sufficient suction power to lift the heavier gold from bedrock. A more reasonable statement would be to say that the dredge has a good recovery rate. The recovery rate of a surface suction dredge is dependent on the expertise of the *operator running it.*

Care must be taken to follow the manufacturer's advice as to pitch or positioning of the sluice box. If the sluice box is tilted too steeply and the fast water is creating a boil, this will be your main sluice robber. Always keep adjusting the tilt or slope until you achieve the correct positioning of the sluice box. When the header box is kept completely full of water while operating, the rocks and gravel will have time to work their way down to the bottom, allowing the gold to become trapped in the riffles. The same method of determining correct sluice box pitch will be fairly applicable to any type surface suction dredge. The common fear of all beginners when gold is not instantly recovered is that the sluice box is losing it. Ninety-nine percent of the time this is wrong; the spot just doesn't have any gold. Practice in areas where gold has been found and learn to avoid this common mistake. Remember, the surface type suction dredge is no *better than the operator*.

Portability is almost as necessary as recovery rate. Weight of any surface type portable dredge seems to take the thrill out of recreational mining almost before you get started. Possibly 99% of the new weekend prospectors are doing it for recreation and the chance to make a few extra dollars. Some do quite well and recovery of from a few pennyweights of gold to an ounce or so is not uncommon. However, recreation and enjoying the great outdoors seem to be the main objectives. If you have to pack unnecessary weight all day, it will not be much fun or recreation. Most manufacturers keep this in mind and try to design equipment as light in weight as possible. Shown is one of the two-inch Oregon "SUPER JET" gold dredges that weighs approximately thirty pounds. Even this feather-weight model seems to get heavier in the evening than it was in the morning! Choose your dredge size carefully, keeping in mind that unless you are a professional and have a permanent claim location to work, you will probably be moving and prospecting around quite a bit. Larger dredge sizes, up to four inches, are quite common and many are in use, but the lightweight two-inch size seems to be the most popular and practical.

I have been dredging with suction dredges for many years, both as a recreational miner and as a professional. I have used about every type built and find that most work fairly well, depending on the knowledge of the operator. The new type by Oregon Gold Dredge, Ltd., is one of the most recent improvements I have noticed in the field. The surface type, ABS plastic sluice box is a real improvement. It allows the operator to achieve maximum recovery of fine gold, but weighs only two to eight pounds. This is extremely helpful when clean-up time arrives. The lightweight plastic sluice box is simply tilted to either side, allowing the material to flow down a built-in groove right into your gold pan or bucket. A few cups of water thrown into the header box will speed this operation considerably and it can be accomplished in a few seconds at most. Clean-up time of approximately a few seconds as compared to fifteen or twenty minutes on the average metal sluice box is indeed a marvel. The ABS plastic sluice box is highly durable and will resist wear, tear and rough handling to a high degree. However, common sense in care should be used with any box, metal or plastic.

The "Super Jet" sluice features a double set of built-in riffles. One standard height, Hungerian Lazy H type and another lower, or smaller, riffle divide each set of the larger riffles. I find this design to be extremely helpful when the heavier concentrations of black sand are encountered. The double set of riffles causes a double action, or reverse boil, and does not allow the riffles to pack solid as is so common on standard boxes.

I am partial to the surface type of sluice box as the recovery rate has always been much better. The underwater type boxes do not seem to be much in use any more; surface types seem to have taken over. This makes the use of any surface type sluice box featuring lighter weight extremely popular. The "Super Jet" sluice box does not require the use of matting or other porous material to be placed under the riffles. This is because the box is constructed in one solid piece, solving the problem of dumping the box and laboriously washing out the matting (commonly called clean-up).

Suction power is always the key to the efficiency of any type of suction dredge. To achieve this there must be a powerful pump. The "Oregon Super Jet" pump really amazes me. Perhaps this is due to the small size of the pump. Anyway, dynamite seems to come in small packages; it does on the "Super Jet" pump. I compared the pressure to my other suction type dredges, and I did not find any of the same approximate size that produced equal pressure. I do not mean this to degrade any manufacturer's equipment; anyone can make this same comparison. Pressure can always be checked with a pressure gauge to test any type pump that lays claim to high pressure or high performance. At any rate, the "Super Jet" pump really produces.

It is possible to use the pump on a small type hydraulic scale as it generates enough force to cut gravel sufficiently. Simply disconnect the hose from the power jet, insert a self-made nozzle, and you have the equivalent of a miniature hydraulic setup. This is always helpful when you need to bring down a bank or overhang in order to get at it with your dredge. Caution should be observed in using this hydraulic process as it is illegal in most areas and will serve only to reduce access to areas now open to the recreational miner.

I wish to extend my thanks to all dredge manufacturers who continually strive to cut the weight and increase production potential of their smaller models. These small suction dredges are the most popular since most of us are now weekenders, and the efficiency rating of these small dredges is all important. The "Oregon Super Jet" can certainly be classed as one of the lightest and one of the most powerful dredges. My thanks go to Oregon Gold Dredge, Ltd., P.O. Box 10214, Eugene, Oregon 97402, for producing this little gem for the recreational miner, prospector, and treasure hunter. For more information on their product and this exciting hobby, write for their catalog.

Several members of The International Treasure Hunting Society spent weeks in Mexico, employing all known prospecting means, including electronic prospecting to locate and recover gold and silver. Charles Garrett, Roy Lagal, George Mroczkowski, and Mexican prospector David Medrano search for silver placer. The Garrett ADS Deepseeker instruments were used to locate nuggets and concentrations of black magnetic sand which were then recovered by the dredge operators. Here the men collect the material from the riffle board. They then pan the material to recover the silver which had accumulated in the black sand pockets. Throughout the trip, much of the ITHS members' time was spent in sharing their knowledge and prospecting techniques with Mexican miners and prospectors.

# CHAPTER XII

# *Conclusion*

The most essential and necessary tool the professional or recreational prospector must have is the faithful gold pan for testing suspect areas. It makes good common sense to have the best device, and the most versatile one, at your disposal. The "Gravity Trap" pan is without question the prospector's most practical friend. It is also used by almost every type of outdoor enthusiast for many different purposes. Many women utilize their Garrett "Gravity Trap" pan as a wall decoration. It has a factory-made hole for wall hanging. Molded into the bottom of the pan is an interesting outdoor scene which brings back memories of our '49'er ancestry. The scene may be highlighted by lightly rubbing silver paint onto it, then wiping off the top surface to achieve a two-tone, engraved effect. Every aspect of the Garrett "Gravity Trap" pan reflects the pride of hand-crafted workmanship.

The Garrett "Gravity Trap" gold pan has proven its usefulness and superior capabilities beyond any doubt. It is used in all gold-bearing regions in the U. S. and it is exported to Australia, England and many other countries abroad. Experienced prospectors have acclaimed it as a true time-saving useful tool, mainly because of its dual-operational capabilities. Our own native America perhaps has more sophisticated and fully-developed mining methods than any other country, and the seasoned prospectors of today truly appreciate any device or tool which tends to reduce time-consuming labor and promotes more efficiency at no added cost. For this reason the "Gravity Trap" pan continues to gain in widespread popularity and use. Its unique and protected design (trade mark registration and patent applications) will insure its continued use for as long as man ventures forth in the quest for golden riches. Gold will always be the world's most coveted precious metal, and some type of gold pan will always be employed in the search for it because panning is one of the fastest and easiest methods of testing.

The "Gravity Trap" pan is no miracle worker, nor was it intended as such; however, the tough plastic construction, the carefully-selected green color and the sharp 90-degree riffles

67

lend themselves to many different successful applications. Electronic prospecting with the metal/mineral detector requires a non-conductive pan. The plastic construction fills this need. The various panning procedures illustrated in this book can be adapted to all personal methods as the sharp 90-degree riffle design saves much time and effort. Regardless of whether plastic tools and electronic prospecting methods fit our preconceived stereotype of the "old burro prospector," modern-day miners and prospectors have accepted both as the most practical, economical and successful tools available. I sincerely hope these simple but explicit instructions have helped the beginner and, perhaps, also made the experienced prospector aware of greater rewards through more modern methods.

Thank you.

Roy Lagal

Pictured above is the prospecting scene engraved on the bottom of the "Gravity Trap" gold pan. Roy Lagal, designer and Charles Garrett, owner of Garrett Electronics and manufacturer of the "Gravity Trap" pan, are combining knowledge of advanced electronics and prospecting expertise to recover placer gold from a cold mountain stream in Colorado. Because these two men recognize the uniqueness of this pan and its value to the prospector they have personally endorsed it.

# APPENDIX

## Where to Find Additional Information on Gold Areas

## STATE BUREAUS OF MINES AND GEOLOGY

Nearly every state in the Union has its Bureau of Mines and Geology. These offices are excellent sources of information on gold-producing areas in a particular state. Some of the addresses are listed below.

Alaska Division of
  Geological Survey
3001 Porcupine Drive
Anchorage, AK 99504

Arizona Bureau of
  Mines and Geology
University of Arizona
Tucson, AZ 85721

California Division of
  Mines and Geology
1416 9th Street
Room 1341
Sacramento, CA 95814

Colorado Geological Survey
1845 Sherman Street
Room 254
Denver, CO 80203

Idaho Bureau of
  Mines and Geology
University of Idaho
Moscow, ID 83843

Montana Bureau of
  Mines and Geology
College of Mineral Science
  and Technology
Butte, MT 59701

Nevada Bureau of
  Mines and Geology
University of Nevada
Reno, NV 89507

New Mexico Bureau of
  Mines and Mineral Resources
Campus Station
Socorro, NM 87801

Oregon Department of Geology
  and Mineral Industries
1069 State Office Building
Portland, OR 97201

South Dakota Geological Survey
Science Center
University of South Dakota
Vermillion, SD 57069

Utah Geological and
  Mineralogical Survey
University of Utah
Salt Lake City, UT 84112

Washington Division of
  Mines and Geology
P. O. Box 168
Olympia, WA 98501

Geological Survey of Wyoming
P. O. Box 3008
University Station
Laramie, WY 82070

## WESTERN FOREST SERVICE REGIONS

To learn whether the area you intend to prospect is open for that activity, study land status maps to find out about open and closed areas. The U. S. Forest Service has land status maps for areas within the boundaries of a National Forest. The names and addresses of the seven Western Forest Service regions are shown below.

ALASKA REGION:
Federal Office Building
P. O. Box 1628
Juneau, AK 99802

CALIFORNIA REGION:
630 Sansome Street
San Francisco, CA 94111

INTERMOUNTAIN REGION:
324 - 25th Street
Ogden, UT 84401

NORTHERN REGION:
Federal Building
Missoula, MT 59807

PACIFIC NORTHWEST
REGION:
319 SW Pine Street
Portland, OR 97208

ROCKY MOUNTAIN
REGION:
11177 - 8th Avenue
Lakewood, CO 80225

SOUTHWESTERN
REGION:
517 Gold Avenue, SW
Albuquerque, NM 87102

## BUREAU OF LAND MANAGEMENT

The Bureau of Land Management (BLM) is under the U. S. Department of Interior. It controls all property outside of the National Forests. If you plan to do a lot of prospecting on these "public lands," or if you have located a good mineral deposit and wish to consider staking a claim, contact your nearest BLM office for additional information. The BLM also has maps showing which areas under their control are open to vehicle traffic, which may be prospected and which may not. The Bureau of Land Management also has a number of helpful brochures on mining laws. If you have any questions, drop them a line and ask for literature. Two bulletins you may want to start with are *Regulations Pertaining to Mining Claims Under the General Mining Laws of 1872* and *Staking a Mining Claim on Federal Lands* (Information Bulletin No. 4-76).

The addresses of the twelve BLM offices follow.

ALASKA STATE OFFICE
555 Cordova St.
Anchorage, AK 99501
(907) 277-1561

ARIZONA STATE OFFICE
2400 Valley Bank Center
Phoenix, AZ 85073
(602) 261-3873

CALIFORNIA STATE
OFFICE
Federal Building
Sacramento, CA 95825
(916) 484-4676

COLORADO STATE OFFICE
Colorado State Bank Building
Denver, CO 80202
(303) 837-4325

EASTERN STATES OFFICE
(All States bordering on and
East of Mississippi River)
7981 Eastern Avenue
Silver Springs, MD 20910
(301) 427-7500

IDAHO STATE OFFICE
Federal Building
Boise, ID 83724
(208) 384-1401

MONTANA STATE OFFICE
(Montana, North &
South Dakota)
Granite Tower Building
222 N. 32nd Street
Billings, MT 59101
(406) 657-6461

NEVADA STATE OFFICE
Federal Building
Reno, NV 59609
(702) 784-5451

NEW MEXICO STATE
OFFICE
(New Mexico, Oklahoma,
& Texas)
Federal Building
Santa Fe, NM 87501
(505) 988-6217

70

OREGON STATE OFFICE
(Oregon & Washington)
729 NE Oregon Street
Portland, OR 97208
(503) 234-4001

UTAH STATE OFFICE
University Club Building
136 E. South Temple Street
Salt Lake City, UT 84111
(801) 524-5311

WYOMING STATE OFFICE
(Wyoming, Nebraska,
& Kansas)
Federal Building
Cheyenne, WY 82001
(307) 778-2326

## OTHER SOURCES

Gold Prospectors Association of
America
P.O. Box 507
Bonsall, CA 92003
(714) 728-6620

Keene Engineering
9330 Corbin Avenue
Northridge, CA 91324
(213) 993-0411

International Treasure Hunting
Society
P.O. Box 3007
Garland, TX 75041
(214) 271-0800

Gem and Treasure Hunting
Association
2493 San Diego Avenue
San Diego, CA 92110
(714) 297-2672

Miners, Inc.
Box 1301
Riggins, ID 83549
(208) 628-3865

*National Prospector's Gazette*
Segundo, CO 81070

*In the Steps of the Treasure
Hunter*
P.O. Box 5
Mule Creek, NM 88051

# A SELECTED READING LIST

Barlee, N. L. *The Guide to Gold Panning in British Columbia: Gold Regions, Methods of Mining and Other Data.* Canada West Publications, 1976.

_____. *Gold Creeks and Ghost Towns: East Kootenay, Boundary, West Kootenay, Okanagan and Similkameen.* Canada West Publications, 1976.

_____. *Historic Treasures and Lost Mines: Of British Columbia.* Canada West Publications, 1976.

_____. *Similkameen: The Pictograph Country.* Canada West Publications, 1978.

_____. Bureau of Mines State Liaison Officers. *Mining and Mineral Operations in the New England and Mid-Atlantic States: A Visitor Guide.* Washington: U. S. Government Printing Office, 1976.

_____. *Mining and Mineral Operations in the North-Central States: A Visitor Guide.* Washington: U. S. Government Printing Office, 1977.

_____. *Mining and Mineral Operations in the Pacific States: A Visitor Guide.* Washington: U. S. Government Printing Office, 1976.

_____. *Mining and Mineral Operations in the South Atlantic States: A Visitor Guide.* Washington: U. S. Government Printing Office, 1976.

Clark, William B. *Gold Districts of California.* (Bulletin 193.) Sacramento: California Division of Mines and Geology, 1976.

Conatser, Estee and von Mueller, Karl. *The Journals of El Dorado: Being a Descriptive Bibliography on Treasure and Subjects Pertaining Thereto. A Waybill to Discovery and Adventure.* Dallas: Ram Publishing Company, 1977.

Dwyer, John N. *Summer Gold: A Camper's Guide to Amateur Prospecting.* New York: Charles Scribner's Sons, 1971.

Eissler, Manvel. *The Metallurgy of Gold.* London: Crosby Lockwood and Son, 1889.

Emmons, William Harvey. *Gold Deposits of the World — With a Section on Prospecting.* New York and London: McGraw-Hill Book Company, Inc., 1937.

Garrett, Charles, and Lagal, Roy. *The Complete VLF/TR Metal Detector Handbook: All About Ground Canceling Metal Detectors.* Dallas: Ram Publishing Company, forthcoming.

Lagal, Roy. *How to Test "Before Buying" Detector Field Guide.* 3d ed., rev. Dallas: Ram Publishing Company, 1978.

_____. *Gold Panning Is Easy.* 2d. ed., rev. Dallas: Ram Publishing Company, 1978.

Marx, Jenifer. *The Magic of Gold.* New York: Doubleday & Company, Inc. 1978.

Muns, George F. *How to Find and Identify the Valuable Metals.* Philadelphia and Ardmore, PA: Dorrance & Company, 1977.

Thornton, Matt. *Dredging for Gold . . . The Gold Divers' Handbook: An Illustrated Guide to the Hobby of Underwater Gold Prospecting.* Northridge, CA: Keene Industries, 1975.

# ARE YOU INTERESTED...

In treasure and coin hunting, relic collecting, ghost-towning, prospecting and/or nugget hunting? For free information on how to get outfitted properly and be successful in the great outdoor hobby of metal detecting or to obtain assistance when you travel, visit one of these established, knowledgeable treasure equipment dealers and suppliers. See the fantastic new VLF/TR DEEPSEEKER!

**ALABAMA: Florence,** John G. Link, 310 Colonial Drive, P.O. Box 682, 35630, (205-766-0087); **Huntsville,** Alabama Treasure Hunter, 909 Chatterson Road, 35802, (205-881-7772); **Mobile,** Confederate Ordnance, 2202 Government Street, P.O. Box 66075, 36606, (205-473-3731)

**ARIZONA: Phoenix,** Lucky Treasure World, 6005-D West Thomas, 85033, (602-247-4506); **Tempe,** The National Treasure Hunters League, 1309 West 21st Street, 85282, (602-968-9295); **Tempe,** The Treasure Shack, 2190 E. Apache, 85281, (602-968-0783); **Tucson,** Morey Detector Sales, 3825 E. Hardy Drive, 85716 (602-323-0071)

**ARKANSAS: Camden,** W. W. Mosley, P.O. Box 7, 768 Crestwood Rd., 71701, (501-836-5314); **Harrison,** Ozark Treasure Hunter League, Industrial Park Rd., 72601, **Little Rock,** Bill's Detectors, 5623 R Street, P.O. Box 7347, 72217, (501-666-6355); **Mountain Home,** Trammell's, 619 Baker Street, 72653, (501-425-3615); **Rogers,** L. L. Lincoln, Route 1, 158 Pyramid Drive, 72756, (501-636-6867); **Royal,** Orchard's Metal Detectors, Fishermens Choice, 6 Mi. From Hot Springs on Hwy 270 West, 71968

**CALIFORNIA: Auburn,** Lo Sierra Mining Equipment, 123 Palm Avenue, 95603, (916-823-1880); **Bakersfield,** C & J Detector Sales, 3104 Pepper Tree Lane, 93309, (805-397-0641); **Bloomington,** Prospector Supplies, 868 Ironwood Avenue, 92316, (714-823-6165); **Brea,** Brea Bicycle & Sporting Goods, 141 S. Brea Blvd., 92621, (714-529-3353); **Buena Park,** Aurora Prospecting Supply, 6286 Beach Blvd., 90620, (714-521-6321); **El Dorado,** Thomas Murry, P.O. Box 406, 6001 Pleasant Valley Road, 95623, (916-622-5245); **Forest Ranch,** Roy Gene Rolls, Hwy. 32 at Sugar Pine, 95942, (916-342-4829); **Fresno,** Fresno Hobby & Crafts, 3026 N. Cedar, 93703, (209-226-4880); **Lafayette,** Fumble Fingers, 1027 Brown Avenue, 94549, (415-284-7406); **Lancaster,** Antelope Acres Market, Ron Farrell, 48011 90th St. West, 93534, (805-948-4190, 942-7165); **Modesto,** Gold Nugget Miner's Supply, 1302-9th Street, 95354, (209-529-5277); **N. Hollywood,** Treasure Emporium, 6507 Lankershim Blvd., 91606, (213-985-5217); **Northridge,** Keene Engineering, Inc., 9300 Corbin, 91324, (213-993-0411); **Riverside,** Pioneer Recoveries, 3510 Audubon Pl., 92501, (714-682-4302); **Rosemead,** Bill & Melba Dibble, 8851 E. Lansford Street, 91770, (213-287-7996); **Salinas,** B. C. Douglass, 1537 Placer Way, 93906, (408-449-1131); **San Bruno,** Dennis E. Witkowsky, Coins and Supplies, P.O. Box 772, 94066, (415-589-8179); **San Diego,** Gem & Treasure Hunting Association, 2493 San Diego Avenue, 92110, (714-297-2672), (Closed Monday & Tuesday); **San Fernando (Lakeview Terrace),** Arts & Hobbies, 12323 Forest Trail, 91342, (213-899-1997); **San Francisco,** Mining & Lapidary, 131 10th Street, 94103, (415-626-6016); **Santa Maria,** Johnny's Metal Detectors, 207 N. Broadway, 93454, (805-922-8703); **Shandon,** Price's Treasures, P.O. Box 201, 93461, (805-238-6487); **Signal Hill,** Hidden Rod Shop, 2623 Gardenia Avenue, 90806, (213-427-8060); **Simi Valley,** Gemstone Equipment, 480 E. Easy Street, 93065, (213-348-6807);

**COLORADO: Englewood,** The Prospectors Cache, 59 W. Girard, 80110, (303-781-8787); **Montrose,** Miner's Mart, 317 East Niagara, 81401, (303-249-8752); **Wheatridge,** C & D Detection Enterprises, 6195 W. 38th Avenue, 80033, (303-424-7780)

**CONNECTICUT: Stratford,** Edward Perchaluk, 304 Circle Drive, 06497, (203-378-1660); **Suffield,** J & E Enterprises, 1242 South Street — Route 75, 06078, (203-668-0029)

**FLORIDA: Fort Lauderdale,** Lawson Studio, 1503 East Las Olas Blvd., 33301, (305-463-5311); **Fort Walton Beach,** James R. Ford Treasure Chest, 528 N. Eglin Pky. 32548, (904-863-1595); **Hallandale,** Silver & Gold Metal Detectors, 24 N.W. First Street, 33009, (305-457-9999); **Jacksonville,** Old Kings Road Treasure Inn, 6946 Old Kings Road So., 32217, (904-733-1928); **Leesburg,** Palm Plaza Cards & Gifts, 713 N. 14th, 32748, (904-787-4661); **Maitland,** Kellyco Detector Distributors, 1443 S. Orlando Avenue, 32751, (305-645-1332); **Melbourne,** Zephyr Treasures, 2898 Zephyr Lane, 32935, (305-254-2796); **Merritt Island,** Mail Order Electronics, 200 Mustang Way 13-B, P.O. Box 1133, 32952, (305-452-8236); **Miami,** Seatech Metal Locators, 985 N.W. 95th Street, 33150, (305-693-1431); **Oakland Park,** Josh Wilson's Detector Sales, 4704 N.E. 17th Avenue, 33334, (305-776-1076); **Pensacola,** Twelfth Avenue Drugs, 2435 N. 12th Avenue, 32503, (904-433-6563); **Tampa,** Carl Anderson, Box 13441, 33611; **Tampa,** Treasure Shack, 3934 Britton Plaza, 33611, (813-833-9841)

**GEORGIA: Atlanta,** Southeastern Treasure Hunters, 985 Woodland Avenue S.E., 30316, (404-627-6019); **East Point,** Ernest M. Andrews, Atlanta Tri-City Area, 2755 Sylvan Rd., 30344, (404-766-8141); **Waycross,** J. C. Ballentine, P. O. Box 761, Hatcher Point Mall, 31501, (912-285-3250).

**IDAHO: Lewiston,** Roy Lagal, Outdoor Hobby Supply, 2416½ E. Main, 83501, (208-743-1768); **Pocatello,** Powers Candy Co., Powers Home Games & Hobbies, 602 S. 1st Avenue, 83201, (208-232-1693).

**ILLINOIS: Bloomington,** Rene's Treasure Trove, 214 East Front Street, 61701, (309-829-4538, 829-4058); **Chebanse,** Jerry's Treasure Hunter's Supply, RR #1, Meents Lane, 60922, (815-939-3815); **Galesburg,** Detectors Unlimited, 1671 Summit Street, 61401, (309-342-4032); **Lombard,** Electronic Exploration, 575 W. Harrison Rd., 60148, (312-620-0618); **Moline,** Hidden Treasure, Rev. John J. Costas, 3116 11th Avenue "A", 61265, (309-797-3098); **Pekin,** Dee's Beauty Shop, 206 Reservoir Rd., 61554, (309-346-4377); **Quincy,** Mid-West Treasure Detectors, 507 So. 8th Street, 62301, (217-223-4757); **Verona,** Gary & Karen Bennett, Indian Trail Rd., 60479, (815-942-5290); **Waukegan,** Tom's Pool Center, Inc., 801 North Green Bay Rd., 60085, (312-244-4505); **Wedron,** Memory House, 1 N. Chestnut Street, 60557, (815-434-3568).

74

**INDIANA: Decatur,** O-D Western Store, Robert A. Everett, RR #5, 46733, (219-724-2097); **Fort Wayne,** A-Z Coins & Stamps, Glenbrook Center, 4201 Coldwater Rd., 46805, (219-483-3743); **Hammond,** J & J Coins, 7019 Calumet Avenue, 46324, (219-932-5818); **Indianapolis,** L & M Sales, 7310 Hazelwood Avenue, 46260, (317-255-4236); **Indianapolis,** The Prospectors Pouch, Indiana Treasure Hunting Headquarters, 246 S. Butler Avenue, 46219, (317-356-7343); **Seymour,** Wray's Treasure Shop, RR #5, 47274, (812-497-2537).

**IOWA: Baxter,** Richard Cross, 314 South Main, 50028, (515-227-3391); **Clear Lake,** Norman Treslan Construction, 4 N. 16th Street, 50428, (515-357-2255); **Indianola,** Herb Dunn Jr., Metal Detector Sales, Route 4, 50125, (515-981-4341); **Tama,** McGrew Oil Co., 120 W. 4th Street, 52339, (515-484-2946, 489-2396).

**KANSAS: Manhattan,** Radio Shack Associate Store, 2609 Anderson Avenue, 66502, (913-539-6151); **Pratt,** Epp's Coin Shop, 112 S. Main Street, 67124, (316-672-6181, 672-6277); **Topeka,** Maxine's Treasure Sales, 5425 SW Wanamaker Road, 66604, (913-862-2872); **Wichita,** Swaim Electronics, 1430 E. Douglas, 67214, (316-262-0077).

**KENTUCKY: Ashland,** Gambill Locksmithing, 1004 Comanche Ct., 41101, (606-325-7931); **Bowling Green,** Thomas D. Brenner Treasure Hunter's, P. O. Box 147, 42101, (502-781-7796); **Louisville,** A. F. Waller, P. O. Box 72083, 40272, (502-937-8008); **Nicholasville,** Paul Phillips, 109 Lake Street, 40356, (606-885-3648).

**LOUISIANA: Benton,** A-Able Treasure Electronics, 102 Duval, 71006, (318-965-0277); **Baton Rouge,** J & F Enterprises, 12211 Greenwell Springs Road, 70814, (504-272-8500); **Delhi,** Hammett & Son Enterprises, Route 1, Box 90, 71232, (318-878-2105); **Metairie,** Henry L. Montegut, 437 Aurora Avenue, 70005, (504-834-2378).

**MARYLAND: Edgewater,** Finders Keepers, John Reichenberg, Route 4, 3316 Oak Drive, 21037, (301-798-1833); **Glenburnie,** Frank's Detectors of Glenburnie, 408 Arbor Drive, 21061, (301-768-3157); **Westover,** Somco Machine Co., Route 1, Box 272, 21871, (301-651-1516, 651-3964).

**MASSACHUSETTS: Agawam,** E & D Electronic Sales & Service, 83 Parker Street, 01001, (413-786-7190); **Auburn,** Found Enterprises, 133 Prospect Street, 01501, (617-832-3721); **Rehoboth,** Larry Violette, Box 74, 02769, (617-252-4497); **W. Springfield,** A. J. Dumais, Dumais Electronics Corporation, 37 Spring Street, 01089, (413-733-9548).

**MICHIGAN: Bay City,** Lloyd R. Buzzard, 1724 E. Salzburg Rd., 48706, (517-684-4765); **Dearborn,** Huffmaster Electronics, 1537 Monroe, 48124, (313-278-7922, 278-1940); **Grand Rapids,** Grant's Book Store, 601 Bridge Street NW, 49504, (616-458-6580); **Lansing,** Finders Keepers Metal Detectors, 2112 Cumberland Road, 48906, (517-321-6594, 323-4250); **Union Lake,** Old Prospectors Shack, 7007 Cooley Lake Road, 48085, (313-363-7328); **Wyoming,** Treasure Hunter's Supply, 3930 Burlingame SW, 49509, (616-538-1957).

**MINNESOTA: Bloomington,** Mid-West Metal Detectors, 8338 Pillsbury Avenue So., 55420, (612-881-5254); **Minneapolis,** Garrett Metal Detector Specialists, 3249 Nicollet Avenue S., 55408, (612-827-3113); **Minneapolis,** Paul's Detector Sales, 4153 31st Avenue S., 55406, (612-724-2154); **St. Paul,** Minnesota Prospectors Supply, Formerly of Red Wing, MN, 902 Goodrich, 55105, (612-226-5118).

**MISSISSIPPI: Jackson,** Eagle Arms Co., 3115 Terry Rd., 39212, (601-373-4557); **Tupelo,** Hobbies Unlimited, P. O. Box 1161, 1219 Nelle Street, 38801, (601-842-6031).

**MISSOURI: Florissant,** The Prospector's Shack, 975 Grenoble Lane, 63033, (314-837-4703); **Hillsboro,** E & R Detector Sales, P. O. Box 213, 63050, (314-789-2078, 586-4263); **Joplin,** Frank's Sales & Service, Route 3, Box 834, 64801, (417-781-6597); **Kansas City,** Clevengers Detector Sales, 8206 North Oak Street Trfwy., 64118, (816-436-0697); **Miller,** Friend's Treasure Outpost, Route 1, 65707, (417-452-2179); **Poplar Bluff,** The Treasure Hut, 1315 North Main, 63901, (314-785-1164); **Springfield,** Radford Jewelers, 1864 South Glenstone, 65804, (417-881-7308); **St. Joseph,** Stanley Johnson Co., 2607 So. 14th, 64503, (816-232-5163); **Warsaw,** Ozark Treasure Chest, P. O. Box 417, 129 Main Street, 65355, (816-438-5445).

**MONTANA: Missoula,** Electronic Parts, 1030 S. Avenue West, P. O. Box 2126, 59801, (406-543-3119).

**NEBRASKA: Ames,** Exanimo Establishment, Main Street, 68621, (402-727-9833, 721-9438); **Sprague,** L. P. Enterprises, Box 46, 68438, (402-794-5730)

**NEVADA: Fallon,** Scott Goodpasture, 9525 Pioneer Way, 89406, (702-867-2015); **Reno,** Sierra Detectors, 419 Flint, 89501, (702-323-2712).

**NEW HAMPSHIRE: Concord,** Don Wilson Sales, 93 So. State Street, 03301, (603-224-5909); **Keene,** Streeter Electronics Metal Detectors Sales, 504 Washington Street, 03431, (603-357-0229); **Seabrook,** The Village Trader, U. S. Route 1, 03874, (603-474-2836).

**NEW JERSEY: Englewood,** General Sales, #10 Humphrey Street, 07631, (201-568-5563); **Saddle Brook,** Geo-Quest, 104 US Hwy. 46, 07662, (201-772-7443); **Trenton,** Treasure Cove, 1055 S. Clinton Avenue, 08611, (609-393-3631, 989-7382).

**NEW MEXICO: Aztec,** Wooley's Trailer Sales, 635 Aztec Boulevard, 87410, (505-334-2871)

**NEW YORK: Fairport,** Lost Coins Enterprise, Darrell C. Kilburn, 721 Mosley Rd., 14450, (716-223-2139); **Geneva,** J. Panna's Electronic Sales, P. O. Box 167, 14456, (315-789-0809); **Glen Cove,** Fred Bond, 2 Leech Circle So., 11542, (516-676-1310); **New York City,** C-T Detectors, 4443 Murdock Avenue, 10466, (212-325-9582); **Walton,** Doc Dave's Treasure Finders, 54 Stockton Avenue, Route 206, 13856, (607-865-5188).

**NORTH CAROLINA: Asheboro,** Treasure World of North Carolina, East Dixie Drive, 27203, (919-629-6164); **Charlotte,** Ernie "Carolina" Curlee Detector Sales Co., Division of Chemation, 3201 Cullman Avenue, 28206, (704-375-8468, 537-5115); **Glen Raven,** Barbee Detector Sales, c/o Barbee Fabrics, Inc., P. O. Box 4235, 27215, (919-584-7781, 584-7873); **Moncure,** B & R Detector Sales, Route 1, Box 185-D, 27559, (919-542-2210, 542-3832); **Wilmington,** Russ Simmons, 414 Biscayne Drive, 28405, (919-686-7009).

**NORTH DAKOTA: Fargo,** Treasure Island, West Acres Shopping Center, 58103, (701-282-4747); **Minot,** Chester N. Iverson, 808 17th Avenue S.W., 58701, (701-838-0149).

**OHIO: Cincinnatti,** J & B Treasures (Northwest Accessories), 2163 Sevenshills Drive, 45240, (513-742-3344); **Cleveland,** Kilian Detector Equipment Company, 1031 Spring Road, 44109, (216-398-4779); **Elyria,** T & K Cycles, 36668 Butternut Ridge Rd., 44035, (216-327-3783); **Lewisburg,** Fox Metal Detectors, Shields Road, RR #2, Box 312 D, 45338, (513-962-2937); **Lima,** Klingler's Rocks 'N Things, 1763 Bowman Road, 45804, (419-227-5294); **Ottawa,** Winkle Radio & TV, Route 4, 17 Mi. N. Lima, 1½ Mi. N. Kalida, Route 115, 45875, (419-532-3957); **Pierpont,** G & D Detector Sales, 6500 North Richmond Road, 44082, (216-577-1496); **Shelby,** Struble Drug Inc. of Shelby, 31 West Main Street, 44875, (419-342-2136, 347-2802); **Waterville,** The Treasure Chest, 3 Mi. W. Waterville, Route 24, 9204 S. River Road, 43566, (419-878-6026).

75

**OKLAHOMA: Jenks,** Woodrow J. Russey, 904 N. Juniper, 74037, (918-299-3551); **Maud,** Dewey's Phillips, 66 Service Station, 301 West King, 74854, (405-374-2786); **Oklahoma City,** Hobby World, 2433 Plaza Prom, Shepherd Mall, 73107, (405-942-4556); **Tulsa,** Ace's Detector Service, 5622 S. Pittsburg, 74135, (918-742-2214).

**PENNSYLVANIA: Greensburg,** Sealand's Metal Detectors, 422 Sells Lane, 15601, (412-834-3429); **Langhorne,** Sonny's Cycle & Sporting Arms, 1964 Maple Avenue, Route 213, 19047, (215-752-3030); **Meadville,** Miller's Treasure & Metal Detectors, RD #1, Pettis Rd., 16335, (814-336-5453); **Morrisdale,** Robert & Cleora Ferguson, P.O. Box 14, Route 53, 16858, (814-342-1268); **New Castle,** Barker Advertising, RD #5, Mitchell Rd., 16105, (412-652-7596); **Williamsport,** K. A. Detectors, RD 4, Box 323, 17701, (717-326-0867).

**RHODE ISLAND: Warwick,** House of Bargains, 345 Warwick Avenue, 02888, (401-781-8580).

**SOUTH CAROLINA: Sumter,** Ken Lyles Detectors, 122 Lazy Lane, 29150, (home — 803-775-8840, office — 775-2806).

**SOUTH DAKOTA: Rapid City,** Donco Metal Detectors, 2424 Canyon Lake Drive, 57701, (605-343-3103)

**TENNESSEE: Chattanooga,** Chattanooga Detector Sales, 3110 3rd Avenue, 37407, (615-622-8882); **Chattanooga,** Hickory Valley Electric Co. and Metal Detector Sales, 6916 Lee Hwy., 37421, (615-892-0525, 892-3581); **Memphis,** Amoneco, 681 Madison, 38103, (901-526-5054); **Memphis,** 38103, (901-526-5054), Mid South Metal Detector Sales, 3179 Northwood Drive, 38111, (901-452-8860); **Nashville,** The Collector's Shop, 100 Oaks Shopping Center; 37204, (615-383-5996); **Selmer,** Selmer Service Station & Sporting Goods, 100 West Court Avenue, 38375, (901-645-5431).

**TEXAS: Amarillo,** J. C. Claxton, 2701 S. Marrs, 79103, (806-383-1613, 374-3820); **Austin,** Niles Carter, 2103 Whitestone Drive, 78745, (512-444-0106); **Beaumont,** Sanders Sports Shop, Route 8, Box G-36, 77705, (713-794-2560); **Brownsville,** Chester's Coin Shop, 2606 International Blvd., 78521, (512-546-4252); **Corpus Christi,** Bayside Metal Detectors, 9245 So. Padre Island Drive, 78418, (512-937-1682, 937-5334); **Dallas,** The Syndicate, 1066 Valley View Center, 75240, (214-233-6694); United Treasure Hunters, 11602 Garland Road, 75218, (214-328-1223); **Donna,** E. David Medrano, 410 So. 23rd Street, 78537, (512-464-4270); **El Paso,** American Camping & Outing Industries, Inc., P. O. Box 12564, 79912, (915-751-7741); **Ft. Worth,** Rex Grove Auto Supply Co., Inc., 4527 E. Belknap, 76117, (817-838-3066, 838-9640); **S. Houston,** Alexander Enterprises, 21 Spencer Highway, 77587, (713-946-6399); **Houston,** Associated Treasure Finders, 15006 Welcome Lane, 77014, (713-440-4333); **Houston,** Research & Recovery, 2803 Old Spanish Trail, 77054, (713-747-4647, 747-4648); **Mission,** Mission Rexall Drug, 1030 Conway Avenue, 78572, (512-585-1532); **San Antonio,** Owens Detector Sales, 5814 Kepler Drive, 78228, (512-434-1605); **Uvalde,** Spurgeon's Artifacts & Coins, 205 W. Nueces, 78801, (512-278-2164); **Wichita Falls,** Eckhart's Detector Sales, 2503 Holliday Street, 76301, (817-767-3939).

**UTAH: Roy,** Bryant T. Cash, 2457 West 4975 South, 84067, (801-825-7858).

**VIRGINIA: Fairfax,** Suburban Detectors, 3169 Spring Street, 22030, (703-273-2542); **Richmond,** Essential Electronics, 10453 Medina Rd., 23235, (804-272-5558); **Virginia Beach,** H & S Detector Center, 2108 Thoroughgood Rd., 23455, (804-464-6072).

**WASHINGTON: Auburn,** Cache Inn Detectors, 17925 S.E. 313th, 98002, (206-631-0466); **Bellingham,** Washington Divers, 903 N. State Street, 98225, (206-676-8029); **Bremerton,** Tanner's Diggin's, 4029 Boundary Trail NW, 98310, (206-377-2532); **Kennewick,** The Coin Cradle Inc., 2810 W. Kennewick Avenue, Suite "E", 99336, (509-735-1507); **Seattle,** Pearl Electronics Inc., 1300 First Avenue, 98101, (206-622-6200); Prospector Ed's Gold Supplies, 5263 Rainier Avenue So., 98118, (206-723-8200); **Spokane,** Bowen's Hideout, S. 1823 Mt. Vernon, 99203, (509-534-4004).

**WISCONSIN: Madison,** Pete's Rock Shop, 1917-19 Winnebago Street, 53704, (608-249-2648).

**WEST VIRGINIA: Paden City,** Murdock's Hobby Shop, 121 N. Fourth Avenue, 26159, (304-337-2711); **Shady Spring,** Ray's Leisure Time Shop, P. O. Drawer E, US Highways, 19 & 21, 25918, (304-763-3110).

**WYOMING: Casper,** Caspar Metal Detectors Sales & Rentals, 1281 Payne and 1017 Cardiff, 82601, (307-235-6323, 234-5205).

**FOREIGN**

**AUSTRALIA, Victoria, Park,** P. J. Bridge Hesperian Detectors, P. O. Box 317, 6100, Western Australia, (09) 38-11762, 32-58575.

**CANADA:**
**ONTARIO,** *Canadian Treasure Trail, P. O. Box 22, Camden East, K0K 1J0, (613-378-6421) *Distributor and Service Center for Canada; **Ayr,** Treasure Unlimited, Box 257, N0V 1E0, (519-632-7955); **Downsview,** Sub-Mariners Diving Equipment, 954 Wilson Avenue, M3K 1E7, (416-630-2590); **Lanark,** Ontario Treasure Seekers, 96 George Street, K0A 1J0 (613-259-2685).

**ALBERTA: Milk River,** Jerry's Detectors, P.O. Box 536, 508-4th Avenue N.E., T0K 1T0, (403-647-3851).

**ONTARIO: Peterborough,** Leisure Detector Sales, Box 44, K9J 6Y5, (705-745-7655).

**ALBERTA: Rocky Mountain House,** Discovery Detectors, Box 1284, T0M 1T0, (403-845-3718).

**ONTARIO: Scarborough,** Pirates Cove, 3274 Danforth Avenue, M1L 1C3, (416-691-5560); **Stirling,** Tall Pines Treasure Trail, Box 186, (613-395-2406); **Strathroy,** L. W. Electronics, Box 42, (519-245-1994).

**BRITISH COLUMBIA, Vancouver,** Diversified Electronics Limited, 1104 Franklin Street, V6A 1J6. (604-254-0761).

**ONTARIO: Waterford,** D. Keith Edwards, RR #5, N0E 1Y0, (519-443-5193).

**SASKATCHEWAN: Yorkton,** John Menken, 67 Darlington Street E., S3N 0C4, (306-783-8336).

**GREAT BRITAIN & IRELAND**
**ENGLAND: London,** *Pieces of Eight, 259 Eversholt Street, N.W.1, (01-388-3686) *Distributor and Service Center for UK, **London,** Treasure World, 155 Robert Street, N.W.1, (01-387-3142).

**MEXICO**
**CALIFORNIA: San Diego,** Gem & Treasure Hunting Association, 2493 San Diego Avenue, 92110, (714-297-2672) (Closed Monday & Tuesday).

**TEXAS: Donna,** E. David Medrano, 410 So. 23rd Street, 78537, (512-464-4270)

**PUERTO RICO: Caparra Terrace-Rio Piedras,** Treasure Hunting Center, 1572 Jesus T. Pinero Avenue, 00921, (809-781-6902)

# RECOMMENDED SUPPLEMENTARY BOOKS

The books described below are among the most popular books in print related to treasure hunting. If you desire to increase your skills in various aspects of treasure hunting, consider adding these volumes to your library.

**DETECTOR OWNER'S FIELD MANUAL.** Roy Lagal. Ram Publishing Company. Nowhere else will you find the detector operating instructions that Mr. Lagal has put into this book. He shows in detail how to treasure hunt, cache hunt, prospect, search for nuggets, black sand deposits . . . in short, how to use your detector exactly as it should be used. Covers completely BFO-TR-VLF/TR types, P.I.'s, P.R.G.'s, P.I.P's, etc. Explains precious metals, minerals, ground conditions, and gives proof that treasure exists because it has been found and that more exists that you can find! Fully illustrated. 236 pages. $6.95.

**ELECTRONIC PROSPECTING.** Charles Garrett, Bob Grant, Roy Lagal. Ram Publishing Company. A tremendous upswing in electronic prospecting for gold and other precious metals has recently occurred. High gold prices and unlimited capabilities of VLF/TR metal detectors have led to many fantastic discoveries. Gold is there to be found. If you have the desire to search for it and want to be successful, then this book will show you how to select (and use) from the many brands of VLF/TR's those that are correctly calibrated to produce accurate metal vs. mineral identification which is so vitally necessary in prospecting. Illustrated. 96 pages. $3.95.

**GOLD PANNING IS EASY.** Roy Lagal. Ram Publishing Company. Roy Lagal proves it! He doesn't introduce a new method; he removes confusion surrounding old established methods. A refreshing NEW LOOK guaranteed to produce results with the "Gravity Trap" or any other pan. Special metal detector instructions that show you how to nugget shoot, find gold and silver veins, and check ore samples for precious metal. This HOW, WHERE and WHEN gold panning book is a must for everyone, beginner or professional! Fully illustrated. 96 pages. $3.95.

**HOW TO TEST "BEFORE BUYING" DETECTOR FIELD GUIDE.** Roy Lagal. Ram Publishing Company. Completely explains the inner workings of the BFO, TR, and discriminator types of detectors. You will learn how to test for sensitivity, stability, total response, wide scan, soil conditions, coils, Faraday shields, and frequency drift, and you will be able to expose incompetent detector engineering and overly enthusiastic, misleading advertising. If you own or are thinking of buying a detector, this book is an ABSOLUTE MUST. Fully illustrated. 64 pages. $3.95.

**THE COMPLETE VLF-TR METAL DETECTOR HANDBOOK** (All About Ground Canceling Metal Detectors). Roy Lagal, Charles Garrett. Ram Publishing Company. The unparalleled capabilities of VLF/TR Ground Canceling metal detectors have made them the number one choice of treasure hunters and prospectors. From History, Theory, and Development to Coin, Cache, and Relic Hunting, as well as Prospecting, the authors have explained in detail the capabilities of VLF/TR detectors and how they are used. Learn the new ground canceling detectors for the greatest possible success. Illustrated. 200 pages. $7.95.

**THE JOURNALS OF EL DORADO.** Estee Conatser, Karl von Mueller. Ram Publishing Company. A descriptive bibliography on treasure and related subjects; a first-of-its-kind storehouse of information devoted exclusively to information of interest to treasure hunters, prospectors, and relic hunters. This book contains approximately 1,800 book listings arranged alphabetically by author. It was developed as a working tool and reference for those in the treasure, small mining, and prospecting fields, especially beginners. Thousands of treasure leads will be found between its covers. Invaluable. 380 pages. $9.95.

**TREASURE HUNTER'S MANUAL #6.** Karl von Mueller. Ram Publishing Company. The original material in this book was written for the professional treasure hunter. Hundreds of copies were paid for in advance by professionals who knew the value of Karl's writing and wanted no delays in receiving their copies. The THM #6 completely describes full-time treasure hunting and explains the mysteries surrounding this intriguing and rewarding field of endeavor. You'll read this fascinating book several times. Each time you will discover you have gained greater in-depth knowledge. Thousands of ideas, tips, and other valuable information. Illustrated. 318 pages. $7.95.

**TREASURE HUNTER'S MANUAL #7.** Karl von Mueller. Ram Publishing Company. The classic! The most complete, up-to-date guide to America's fastest growing activity, written by the old master of treasure hunting. This is *the* book that fully describes professional methods of RESEARCH, RECOVERY, and TREASURE DISPOSITION. Includes a full range of treasure hunting methods from research techniques to detector operation, from legality to gold dredging. Don't worry that this material overlaps THM #6 . . . both of Karl's MANUALS are 100% different from each other but yet are crammed with information you should know about treasure hunting. Illustrated. 334 pages. $7.95.

**SUCCESSFUL COIN HUNTING.** Charles Garrett. Ram Publishing Company. The best and most complete guide to successful coin hunting, this book explains fully the how's, where's, and when's of searching for coins and related objects. It also includes a complete explanation of how to select and use the various types of coin hunting metal detectors. Based on more than twenty years of actual in-the-field experience by the author, this volume contains a great amount of practical coin hunting information that will not be found elsewhere. Profusely illustrated with over 100 photographs. 248 pages. $6.95.

**TREASURE HUNTING PAYS OFF!** Charles Garrett. Ram Publishing Company. This book will give you an excellent introduction to all facets of treasure hunting. It tells you how to begin and be successful in general treasure hunting; coin hunting; relic, cache, and bottle seeking; and prospecting. It describes the various kinds of metal/mineral detectors and tells you how to go about selecting the correct type for all kinds of searching. This is an excellent guidebook for the beginner, but yet contains tips and ideas for the experienced TH'er. Illustrated. 88 pages. $3.95.

**THE COMPLETE BOOK OF COMPETITION TREASURE HUNTING.** Ernie "Carolina" Curlee. Ram Publishing Company. This book gives the details you need to know to sponsor or compete successfully in an organized treasure hunt. All about everything from choosing a name for a hunt and promoting it to receiving the prize you may have won. Whole sections on "How To Sponsor" and "How To Win." Every metal detector owner/treasure hunter can benefit from Ernie's down-to-earth, plainly written information and instructions. A book that will pay for itself many times over! Fully illustrated. 88 pages. $5.95.

**PROFESSIONAL TREASURE HUNTER.** George Mroczkowski. Ram Publishing Company. Research is 90 percent of the success of any treasure hunting endeavor. You will become a better treasure hunter by learning how, through proper treasure hunting techniques and methods, George was able to find treasure sites, obtain permission to search (even from the U. S. Government), select and use the proper equipment, and then recover treasure in many instances. If treasure was not found, valuable clues and historical artifacts were located that made it worthwhile or kept the search alive. Profusely illustrated. 132 pages. $6.95.

# International Treasure Hunting Society

The International Treasure Hunting Society (ITHS) publishes a quarterly journal, THE INTERNATIONAL TREASURE HUNTER. Each issue contains carefully selected "how to" information regarding treasure hunting, metal detecting, prospecting, relic hunting, and other projects, as well as the latest successful treasure hunting stories of treasures found world-wide. Other information about treasure-hunting clubs and competition treasure hunts is also included. Copies are distributed free to ITHS members. Non-members may purchase one or more publications from Ram Publishing Company for $1.50 each. Copies may also be ordered direct from ITHS, P.O. Box 3007, Garland, Texas 75041. Obtain information about ITHS by writing the same address or by calling 214-271-0800.

**THE INTERNATIONAL TREASURE HUNTER,** Vol. 1, No. 1. This premier issue contains complete information regarding the organization and founding of the ITHS. Several informative articles include, "Electronic Treasure Hunting: The First Fifty Years," "Europe: A Treasure Hunter's Paradise!," and "The Soldier's Legacy, Searching for Battlefield Relics." These are but three of the articles included in this first issue which has now become a collector's item. $1.50 each.

**THE INTERNATIONAL TREASURE HUNTER,** Vol. 2, No. 1. This second issue has numerous "how to" articles, including a special coin hunting article by famed treasure hunter T. R. Edds. Read this article to learn how to "Unlock Ocean Beach Treasure Vaults." Other special articles tell about gold hunting in Australia, the First International Championship Treasure Hunt, and the first treasure hunter to search the ghost town of Spring Creek, Colorado. There are many other articles. $1.50 each.

# BOOK ORDER BLANK

See your detector dealer or bookstore or send check or money order directly to Ram for prompt, postage paid shipping, bookpost. If not completely satisfied return book(s) within 10 days for a full refund.

____ DETECTOR OWNER'S FIELD MANUAL **$6.95**

____ ELECTRONIC PROSPECTING **$3.95**

____ GOLD PANNING IS EASY **$3.95**

____ HOW TO TEST "BEFORE BUYING" DETECTOR FIELD GUIDE **$3.95**

____ COMPLETE VLF-TR METAL DETECTOR HANDBOOK (THE) (ALL ABOUT GROUND CANCELING METAL DETECTORS) **$7.95**

____ JOURNALS OF EL DORADO (THE) **$9.95**

____ TREASURE HUNTER'S MANUAL #6 **$7.95**

____ TREASURE HUNTER'S MANUAL #7 **$7.95**

____ SUCCESSFUL COIN HUNTING **$6.95**

____ TREASURE HUNTING PAYS OFF! **$3.95**

____ COMPLETE BOOK OF COMPETITION TREASURE HUNTING (THE) **$5.95**

____ PROFESSIONAL TREASURE HUNTER **$6.95**

____ INTERNATIONAL TREASURE HUNTER, Vol. 1, No. 1 **$1.50**

____ INTERNATIONAL TREASURE HUNTER, Vol. 2, No. 1 **$1.50**

Please add 35¢ for each book ordered (to a maximum of $1.00) for handling charges.

| | |
|---|---|
| Total for Items | $ _____ |
| Texas Residents Add 5% State Tax | _____ |
| Handling Charge | _____ |
| Total of Above | $ _____ |

ENCLOSED IS MY CHECK OR MONEY ORDER $ _____

NAME _____

ADDRESS _____

CITY _____

STATE _____ ZIP _____

PLACE MY NAME ON YOUR MAILING LIST ☐

RAM BOOKS

Ram Publishing Company
P.O. Drawer 38649, Dallas, Texas 75238
**Dept. GP5**
214-278-8439
DEALER INQUIRIES WELCOME

# FIELD NOTES

# FIELD NOTES

# FIELD NOTES

# FIELD NOTES

## Ram Publications

*Complete Book of Competition Treasure Hunting (The)*
  Learn the INSIDE FACTS and you, too, can become a WINNER.

*Complete VLF-TR Metal Detector Handbook (The)*
  THE OPERATIONAL/TECHNICAL MANUAL . . . thoroughly
  explains VLF/TR metal/mineral detectors and HOW TO USE them.
  Compares VLF/TR's with all other types.

*Detector Owner's Field Manual*
  The world's most complete field guide. Explains the total
  capabilities and HOW TO USE procedures of all types of metal
  detectors.

*Electronic Prospecting*
  Learn how to find gold and silver veins, pockets, and nuggets using
  easy electronic metal detector methods.

*Gold Panning Is Easy*
  This excellent field guide shows you how to FIND and PAN gold as
  quickly and easily as a professional.

*"How to Test" Detector Field Guide*
  Learn how to find QUALITY before you buy . . . BFO, TR,
  VLF/TR, and discriminators.

*Journals of El Dorado (The)*
  The most misunderstood treasure hunting book. An invaluable
  research tool. Study this book and FIND TREASURE.

*Professional Treasure Hunter*
  Discover how to succeed with PROFESSIONAL METHODS,
  PERSISTENCE, and HARD WORK.

*Successful Coin Hunting.*
  The world's most authoritative guide to FINDING VALUABLE
  COINS with all types of metal detectors. The name speaks for
  itself!

*Treasure Hunter's Manual #6*
  Quickly guides the inexperienced beginner through the mysteries of
  FULL TIME TREASURE HUNTING.

*Treasure Hunter's Manual #7*
  The classic! THE book on professional methods of RESEARCH,
  RECOVERY, and DISPOSITION of treasures found.

*Treasure Hunting Pays Off!*
  An excellent introduction to all facets of treasure hunting.